A PRACTICAL APPROACH TO SYSTEMS ELECTRONICS

G000153841

J. M. Gregory M.A., D.Phil.

Winchester College

R. Q. Hackett M.A., D.Phil.

Christ's Hospital

C. Vincent-Smith B.Sc.

Christ's Hospital

Longman

LONGMAN GROUP LIMITED
*Longman House, Burnt Mill, Harlow, Essex CM20 2JE, England
and Associated Companies throughout the World*

First published 1985
ISBN 0 582 35500 1

Set in Monophoto Times New Roman

*Printed in Great Britain
by Butler and Tanner Ltd, Frome and London*

Contents

About this book

To the teacher

This book has two aims. The first one is to cover the electronics required for the various A level physics courses. This is done in chapters 1 to 6. The second aim is to introduce students to the ideas and the jargon of electronics to enable them to read data sheets and further literature with understanding and confidence. The last two chapters are intended to stimulate ideas and to provide circuits for project work. The material should also be of use for O, AO and A level electronics courses.

We have introduced the important concepts through a limited number of circuits, all of which are intended to be studied experimentally. The order of presentation is different from most books, in that integrated circuits are introduced before discrete components. This has been done for two reasons: firstly, because their characteristics are simpler to understand, and secondly, because after a comparatively short time students will be able to construct a whole range of different systems from these versatile building blocks. Discrete components, such as the transistor, are only introduced to extend the variety of problems and projects which can be solved. There is no discussion of the physics of semiconductor materials nor of the transistor voltage amplifier and, in general, standard A level physics theory is not included: the student is expected to consult A level physics textbooks for this.

The text contains a range of questions related to the practical work to test understanding and application of the concepts and devices introduced. Answers and/or guides to practical solutions are given on pages 75–85.

We have tried to keep the equipment required to a minimum. For this reason we suggest that all the circuits are built on solderless 'breadboard' (the cover picture shows a typical circuit). This seems to be the cheapest and most flexible method of construction, though most of the circuits can be built with commercially available modules. The digital practical work can be carried out using either TTL or CMOS integrated circuits (see section 1.3).

To the student

This book covers a wide range of practical electronic circuits and contains background information to help you understand how they work. The experiments are concerned with making circuits do a job, not with the physics of semiconductors. You should set up as many of the circuits as possible – it is much easier to understand how a circuit works when you have it working in front of you.

When working through the experiments, always draw an accurate and complete circuit or block diagram in your notebook. Also record all the measurements you make, including the time base and Y-scale settings on the oscilloscope when you observe waveforms and pulse shapes. Once you are out of the laboratory, your notebook becomes your only record of the experiments you have done. At the same time, try to work through the questions. They are there to amplify the text and to increase your understanding of what is happening.

You will need access to a standard A level physics textbook if you do not already understand the following parts of current electricity theory:
(a) calculations based on Ohm's law;
(b) the calculation of energy dissipated in resistors;

(c) the use of potential dividers and potentiometers;
(d) the use of capacitors to store charge, and calculations based on $C = Q/V$;
(e) the charging and discharging of a capacitor through a resistor;
(f) calculations based on the time constant, RC;
(g) the amplitude and r.m.s. value of an alternating voltage or current.

Much of the mathematics contained in this book is not essential detail for A level physics, although the results of the mathematical reasoning are important and should be remembered. If you can understand the Boolean algebra and the analyses for the operational amplifier circuits, you will obtain a much firmer grasp of the subject.

One piece of advice: set up your circuits with care. One wrong connection can take an awfully long time to find.

Units

SI units are used in the text of the book, but a British Standards code is used for labelling the resistors and capacitors in the circuit diagrams. This is the notation likely to be encountered in current electronics literature. Examples of it are given in the table.

SI notation	BS code
$1\,\Omega$	1R0
$4.7\,\Omega$	4R7
$47\,\Omega$	47R
$100\,\Omega$	100R
$1\,k\Omega$	1K0
$10\,k\Omega$	10K
$100\,k\Omega$	100K
$1\,M\Omega$	1M0
$500\,pF$	500p
$10\,nF$	10n
$4.7\,\mu F$	4μ7
$2.2\,mF$	2m2

Symbols for circuit diagrams

Some of the symbols used in the circuit diagrams and logic diagrams in this book are shown below.

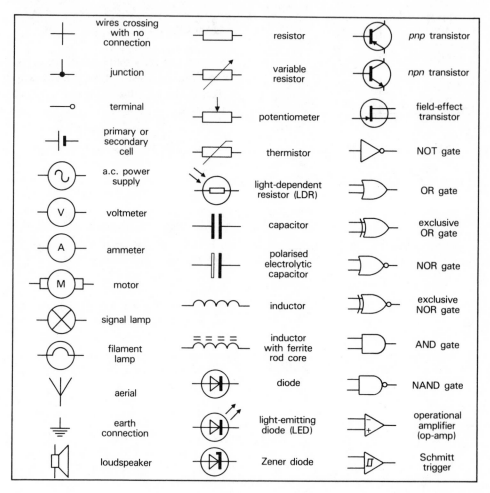

wires crossing with no connection	resistor	pnp transistor
junction	variable resistor	npn transistor
terminal	potentiometer	field-effect transistor
primary or secondary cell	thermistor	NOT gate
a.c. power supply	light-dependent resistor (LDR)	OR gate
voltmeter	capacitor	exclusive OR gate
ammeter	polarised electrolytic capacitor	NOR gate
motor	inductor	exclusive NOR gate
signal lamp	inductor with ferrite rod core	AND gate
filament lamp	diode	NAND gate
aerial	light-emitting diode (LED)	operational amplifier (op-amp)
earth connection	Zener diode	Schmitt trigger
loudspeaker		

1 Getting started

1.1 Introduction

The purpose of this book is to introduce you to the basic building blocks of electronics circuits. With this knowledge, you will be able to construct more elaborate circuits and to appreciate some of the subtleties included in more advanced designs.

Electronic circuits are broadly classified into two categories: *digital* and *analogue*. The first three chapters look at simple digital systems constructed from combinations of logic elements. These are all *switch* circuits, i.e. each element has only two states, 'on' and 'off'. The fourth chapter is about basic operational amplifier circuits – the analogue category. Digital circuits are introduced before analogue ones because, with only a 'two-state' signal, they are easier to understand. Integrated circuit operational amplifiers and logic elements contain circuits made of diodes and transistors. Diodes and transistors are also used as separate discrete components coupled to the integrated circuits. How and why this is done is explained in chapter 5. The book ends with chapters on radio, digital and analogue systems, which link together many of the ideas, circuits and techniques of earlier chapters.

Digital clocks and the arithmetic and memory functions in electronic calculators are examples of digital systems. The full circuits are rather elaborate but are only made up of large numbers of the simple logic devices that you will study in this book. In digital circuits, information is converted into, and processed as, signals with only two states, 'on' and 'off' (also known as 'logic 1' and 'logic 0'). The familiar sequence of traffic lights can be produced by a simple digital system. You will construct a circuit to simulate this in chapter 7.

This chapter now continues with two sections about equipment and families of integrated circuits before the first experiments are introduced in section 1.4.

1.2 The breadboard

Most of the leading manufacturers of educational equipment supply ranges of electronic modules where boards containing integrated circuits (ICs) can be

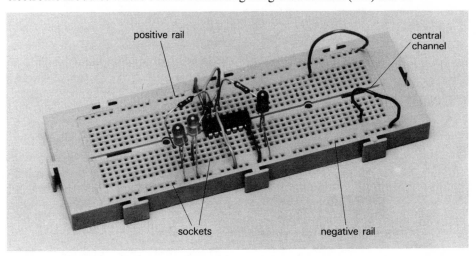

Figure 1.1   A breadboard

connected together to construct the various circuits. It is possible to use these to perform all of the tasks described in this book. However, the authors have found from experience that the use of a solderless 'breadboard' (where individual ICs, resistors and transistors are pushed into interconnecting sockets) leads to greater versatility and ease in designing circuits, and is also considerably cheaper. Circuits can be assembled, corrected and extended rapidly and easily. The same components can also be used again and again if they are inserted and removed from the board with care.

Figure 1.1 shows one of the popular breadboards. There are 47 vertical rows of 5 interconnecting sockets on both sides of a central insulating channel. At the top and bottom of the board are single horizontal rows of 40 interconnected sockets, to act as the positive and negative (or 0 V) supply rails. The holes are spaced so that standard ICs can be fitted across the central channel.

1.3   Families of ICs and power supplies

The digital practical work can be carried out using either of the two families of digital ICs, which are called CMOS (Complementary Metal Oxide Semiconductor) and TTL (Transistor–Transistor Logic). CMOS has the advantage that it will work from any d.c. supply between 3 and 15 V, whereas TTL must have a regulated 5 V supply (the first diagram on page 72 shows a suitable circuit for this). For work with CMOS circuits, a standard 9 V dry battery is suitable. The disadvantages of CMOS are that it can be damaged by static charge building up on the input pins and that connections to the power supply must always be made first. On the other hand, TTL ICs are very robust and can withstand rough handling and higher currents. The practical instructions in this book are written so that you use any one of the following three systems.

System 1 TTL with a regulated 5 V supply;
System 2 CMOS with a 9 V supply;
System 3 CMOS with a 5 V supply interfaced with TTL.

The logic box circuits in appendix II, which use 5 V supplies, will drive both TTL and CMOS (i.e. systems 1 and 3). However, it is not a good idea for beginners to mix CMOS and TTL ICs ('chips') in the same circuit in general, so always try to keep to one family, unless you are instructed to do otherwise. You will be told about important distinctions between the systems and families when necessary.

In this book, the positive rail value for most digital circuits will be written as V^+, which will be either 5 V or 9 V, depending on the system you are using.

1.4   Indicators and the NOT gate or inverter

In digital circuits, *light-emitting diodes* (LEDs) are useful for indicating the states of inputs and outputs, which are either 'high' or 'low' (logic 1 or 0). For example, green LEDs can be used for inputs and red ones for outputs. The potential difference across a typical LED is 2 V. The current drawn is about 10 mA, so the LED can be connected across a 5 V supply in series with a 270 Ω resistor (see figure 1.2). Looking at the LED with the pins upwards, the flat on the circular body is close to the cathode (negative) pin.

The simplest logic gate is the NOT gate or inverter (see figure 1.3). Insert a hex inverter IC (an IC with six inverter circuits on it) across the central channel of the breadboard with pin 1 at the lower left-hand corner. `7404` `4069` * Connect leads between pins 14 and the V^+ rail and between pin 7 and the 0 V rail (look at the pin-out chart in appendix I to locate the pins). Colour code the leads for ease of

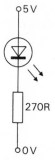

Figure 1.2

Question

1 Use $R = (V^+ - V_{LED})/I$ to calculate the minimum value of limiting resistor required for an LED that draws 15 mA and is connected to a 9 V supply.

Figure 1.3   The NOT gate or INVERTER

input, A	output, Y
1	0
0	1

(a) Symbol   (b) Truth table

---

* These panels give the numbers of the integrated circuits you will need to do the practical work described. The first panel gives the numbers of the TTL components, and the second the numbers of the CMOS equivalents.

recognition, using, for example, red and black for power supplies, green and yellow for inputs, blue for outputs, etc. (this is particularly helpful in more complicated circuits). Power supply rails and connections to them are not normally shown in circuit diagrams although they are always required. It is therefore wise to *power up* each IC as soon as it is connected to the board, as it is very easy to forget these connections. If you forget them, you will drive the CMOS IC through its inputs rather than the power leads, which can lead to disaster.

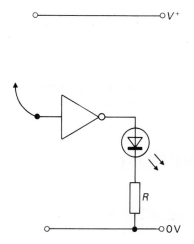

Figure 1.4

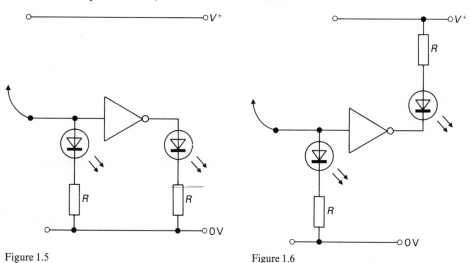

Figure 1.5

Figure 1.6

Connect the anode (positive) pin of the LED to pin 12 and the cathode to 0 V through resistor R (270 Ω for a 5 V supply and 680 Ω for 9 V) (see figure 1.4). For TTL 7404 the LED should not light, indicating logic 0. This is because pin 13 is 'floating', i.e. not connected. *For all TTL ICs, unconnected input pins are always at logic 1.* So for simple breadboard circuits it is safe to leave TTL inputs floating if they are meant to be at logic 1. For CMOS circuits or TTL permanent circuits, every pin must be connected. *All unused CMOS pins must be connected to either 0 V or V^+.*

For CMOS 4069 (and TTL 7404), connect another resistor R and LED between pin 13 and 0 V, as in figure 1.5. The output LED (the first one) will light, indicating logic 1. The input LED is off. Now connect pin 13 to V^+. The output LED is off, indicating logic 0. Notice that the energy for the output comes from the power supply connections, not from the input connections.

The operation of a logic device is usually shown by writing down what is called its *truth table*. This lists the output of the device for all possible combinations of the inputs. A truth table for the inverter is shown in figure 1.3. In your circuit, a lit LED indicates logic 1. Now reconnect the output circuit to the gate as shown in figure 1.6. Now the LED lights for an output of logic 0. This is called *inverse logic*.

If you are using system 3 (see section 1.3) you will have noticed that the output LED is very dim. For this system, you must use a complete inverse logic circuit on the output of a gate (see figure 1.7), instead of the single LED. The LED in this circuit will always light brightly.*

Construct a four-LED indicator unit, using the gates on one TTL 7404 hex inverter IC with four 1 kΩ input resistors, for future use. This four-LED indicator unit will also be needed with system 1 in many circuits. To make a similar unit for system 2 using CMOS 4069, change the input resistor to 10 kΩ and use 680 Ω as the safety resistor with the LED. This indicator unit will be signified by the symbol ∎ when it is needed in chapters 2, 3 and 7.

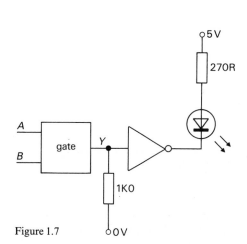

Figure 1.7

* Even this arrangement may not be suitable in all circuits. System 3 operates very close to the lower switching limit of the CMOS chip, and if the output has to switch another CMOS input as well as lighting the LED (as, for example, in the shift register circuits in chapter 7), it may not do so every time. An alternative arrangement, which will always work, is to use a transistor to drive each LED, as described in section 3.2.

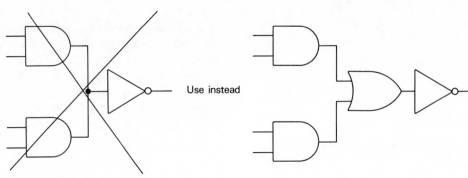

Figure 1.8

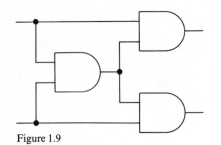

Figure 1.9

One last rule to remember: *never connect more than one output to the same input* (see figure 1.8). However, several inputs *can* be driven from the same output (as in figure 1.9, for example).

1.5   The AND, NAND, OR and NOR gates

The four basic two-input logic gates are shown in figure 1.10, together with their symbols and truth tables. `7408, 7400, 7432, 7402` `4081, 4011, 4071, 4001` Place each IC on the breadboard in turn, and check the corresponding truth table using the same arrangement as for the NOT gate in section 1.4. (You will now need two input LEDs and resistors.) It helps to become familiar with the arrangement of gates within each IC. Notice that the four NOR gates on TTL 7402 are in the reverse direction to the gates on the other three TTL ICs. If you are using CMOS gates, you will see that their outputs are always the middle pins.

AND	$\frac{A}{B}$ ⟩— Y	$Y = 1$ if $A = 1$ AND $B = 1$
NAND	$\frac{A}{B}$ ⟩o— Y	$\bar{Y} = 1$ if $A = 1$ AND $B = 1$ or $Y = $ NOT $(A$ AND $B)$
OR	$\frac{A}{B}$ ⟩— Y	$Y = 1$ if $A = 1$ OR $B = 1$
NOR	$\frac{A}{B}$ ⟩o— Y	$\bar{Y} = 1$ if $A = 1$ OR $B = 1$ or $Y = $ NOT $(A$ OR $B)$
NOT	A ▷o— Y	$\bar{Y} = 1$ if $A = 1$ or $Y = $ NOT A

inputs		output, Y					
		operation	AND	NAND	OR	NOR	NOT
A	B	Boolean expression	$A.B$	$\overline{A.B}$	$A+B$	$\overline{A+B}$	$\bar{A}$
0	0		0	1	0	1	1
0	1		0	1	1	0	1
1	0		0	1	1	0	0
1	1		1	0	1	0	0

Figure 1.10   Logic gates and their truth tables

The Boolean expressions are included in figure 1.10 for future reference. The notation is a useful shorthand method to describe the operations of the gates, '$\bar{A}$' means 'NOT A'; '$A.B$' means 'A AND B'; '$A+B$' means 'A OR B'. Section 2.2 contains further information about Boolean algebra.

You will soon see that it is useful to be able to use a two-input gate as a one-input gate. The unused input can be connected

(a)   to the logic level that will not alter the function of the gate (this will be logic 1 for AND and NAND gates and logic 0 for a NOR gate), or

(b)   to another input of the same gate that *is* being used.

Each of the four gates in figure 1.11 is acting as a NOT gate.

Connect a NOT gate to each input of a NAND gate, as in figure 1.12. Write down a truth table relating the inputs A and B to the output Y. Which single gate has the

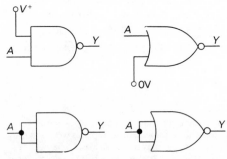

Figure 1.11   NOT gates

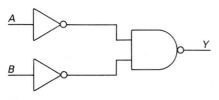

Figure 1.12

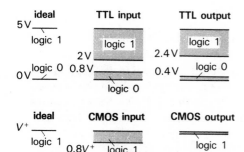

Figure 1.13   Logic levels for TTL and CMOS

Figure 1.14   Transfer characteristics

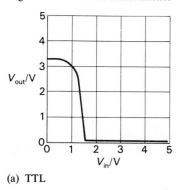

(a)   TTL

same truth table as this? (Look back at figure 1.10.) Show that connecting the two inputs of a NAND gate together, as in figure 1.11, makes a NOT gate. You should now see that an OR gate can be made from three NAND gates.

Add a fourth NAND gate to make the OR into a NOR gate. It is not possible to use fewer than four NAND gates to make a NOR gate.

A three-input AND or OR gate can be made from two two-input AND or OR gates. Make one by connecting the output of one gate to one of the inputs of the other.

Questions

2 Construct an AND gate from NAND gates.
3 What is the difference between '(NOT A) AND (NOT B)' and 'NOT (A AND B)'?

1.6   The transfer (input–output voltage) characteristic of a logic gate

This section is intended to help you acquire a better understanding of the conditions for a gate to switch between logic states.

The voltage ranges for logic 1 and logic 0 states for TTL and CMOS gates are shown in figure 1.13. These ranges can be measured for a NOT gate by either of the following standard methods. `7404` `4069`

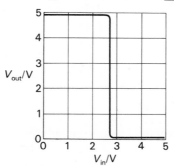

(b)   CMOS

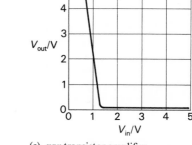

(c)   *npn* transistor amplifier

(a)   Vary the input p.d. V_{in}, so that you can plot a graph of V_{in} against V_{out}, which should be similar to the appropriate transfer characteristic shown in figure 1.14. Figure 1.15 shows a suitable circuit, which uses a 5 kΩ potentiometer. The characteristic of a third inverting device – the single transistor amplifier, connected as shown in figure 1.16 – has been included in figure 1.14 for future reference.

(b)   You can display the transfer characteristics directly on an oscilloscope screen by using the circuit in figure 1.17. A signal generator or low-voltage transformer

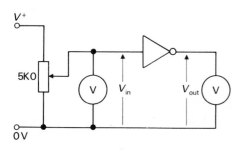

Figure 1.15   Circuit for measuring the transfer characteristic

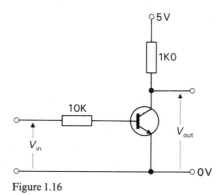

Figure 1.16

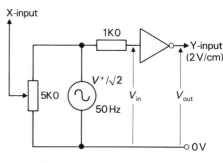

Figure 1.17   Circuit for displaying the transfer characteristic

capable of delivering peak signal V^+ is connected to the X-input of the oscilloscope (time base switched off) so that the X-deflection of the spot is proportional to V_{in}. The Y-input, connected as shown, will be proportional to V_{out}. The traces will also show the result of having negative V_{in}. Centre the spot on the screen to define the axes before connecting the oscilloscope to the circuit.

1.7   Simple control circuits

The inverter can be used as a simple switch in a control circuit. When the input p.d. swings over a sufficient range, the output p.d. of the gate will change from high to low or from low to high (see figure 1.14). Set up the circuit in figure 1.18. `7404` `4069` Adjust the 5 kΩ variable resistor until the LED is just extinguished. The NOT gate will give a high output when the light-dependent resistor (LDR) is covered, i.e. dark. Rearrange the circuit so that the LED goes off rather than on when the LDR is darkened. There are two ways of doing this: one by changing the input circuit, the other by changing the output circuit. You will need to readjust the 5 kΩ resistor, or even omit it (TTL input case).

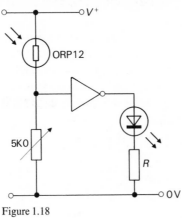

Figure 1.18

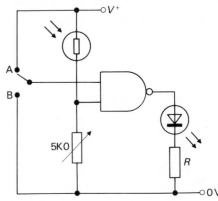

Figure 1.19

A temperature control circuit can be constructed by replacing the LDR by a thermistor such as the TH–3. The resistance of this device changes exponentially with temperature so it can be used to switch an oven on or off, for example, at a temperature determined by the 5 kΩ variable resistor.

For a rapid switching action, a Schmitt trigger inverter (TTL 7414 or CMOS 40106) is normally used. The property of this IC is discussed in section 4.11 and it is used in chapter 7.

Replace the NOT gate in figure 1.18 by a NAND gate. `7400` `4011` There are two ways that the NAND gate can be connected to act as a NOT gate (see figure 1.11). The upper method of figure 1.11 gives an extra facility to the circuit, called an *enable* or *disable* function. With the switch in position A (see figure 1.19), the circuit is enabled. In position B, it is disabled: the output of the NAND gate is always high, whatever the state of the other input. AND, OR and NOR gates can be used to provide similar functions.

Questions

4 Explain how the LDR circuit in figure 1.18 works.
5 Redesign the circuit in figure 1.19 to perform the same function using an AND gate. Is position A of the switch in the AND gate circuit the enable position or the disable position?

1.8   Further questions

1 Design AND, OR and NAND functions using only NOR gates.
2 Use truth tables to prove that each of the gates shown in figure 1.11 is acting as a NOT gate. The NOR gate has an $\overline{enable}$, i.e. one input must be grounded for the output to be able to change, whereas the NAND gate has an *enable*. Can AND gates and OR gates be enabled? If so, is the enable input connected to logic 1 or logic 0?

3 Write out a truth table for each of the following and implement them using two-input NAND gates:

(a) $Y = \text{NOT}\,(A\text{ OR }B)$;

(b) $Y = (\text{NOT }A)\text{ OR }(\text{NOT }B)$;

(c) $Y = \text{NOT}\,((\text{NOT}A)\text{ OR }B)$;

(d) $Y = \text{NOT}\,((\text{NOT }A)\text{ OR }(\text{NOT }B))$.

4 Design a three-input AND gate using only two-input NAND gates.

Figure 1.20

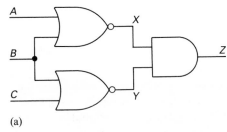

(a)

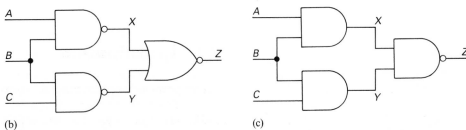

(b)

(c)

5 Write out truth tables for the outputs X, Y and Z for the eight possible combinations of inputs A, B and C to the logic diagrams in figures 1.20(a), (b) and (c). What is each of these circuits?

6 Design a four-input AND gate using only two-input gates.

7 Design a system where the indicator LED lights only when input $A = 0$ and input B or input $C = 1$.

8 (a) The resistance of thermistor T in figure 1.21 decreases with increasing temperature. R_1 is chosen so that the indicator is off at a given temperature. In the circuit shown, will the indicator light for too high or too low a temperature? Must the switch be in position A or position B for the circuit to function?

(b) Design a circuit which will light the indicator when the temperature of an oven is outside a given range, i.e. either too high or too low. Assume that two thermistors, two resistors R_1 and R_2 and any one of the two-input logic gates are available. State whether R_1 and/or R_2 must be greater than, equal to or less than the resistance of T at the oven's normal temperature.

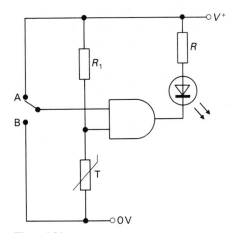

Figure 1.21

2 Combinational logic

2.1 Introduction

In *combinational* logic circuits, the outputs at any time are determined entirely by the state of the inputs. In chapter 3, a different class of circuits, involving *sequential* logic, will be introduced where this is no longer true. The simplest combinational logic circuits are those covered in section 1.5, where the inputs or output of a single gate are inverted. Any combinational logic problem can be completely specified by a truth table. Alternatively, a Boolean expression relating the output to the inputs can be written down and simplified. This is done either by using Boolean algebra or by making all of the gates in the expression from NAND or NOR gates and then cancelling out redundant pairs of gates. Examples of both methods are given below.

An essential core element of a computer or microprocessor called the *arithmetic logic unit* (ALU) is made from a number of logic gates. It adds, subtracts, multiplies and compares numbers for equality or inequality. The separate combinational logic circuits required for each of these functions are the connecting theme of this chapter.

2.2 Boolean algebra

Boolean algebra is usually quicker and easier to use than truth tables, which can be a very tedious method of solving problems. The rules are quite simple and enable complicated expressions to be simplified to show the combination of simple gates required for a circuit. Boolean notation was introduced in figure 1.10: '$\overline{A}$' means 'NOT A'; '$A.B$' means 'A AND B'; '$A+B$' means 'A OR B'.

All the logic identities needed for simple analysis problems are given below. Verify some of them, using the truth tables for the two-input gates (figure 1.10).

(a) For two-input gates where one or both inputs A are variable (0 or 1):

$$\begin{array}{lllll}
\text{AND} & A.0 = 0 & \text{OR} & A+0 = A & \text{NOT} \quad \overline{1} = 0 \\
& A.1 = A & & A+1 = 1 & \overline{0} = 1 \\
& A.A = A & & A+A = A & \overline{\overline{A}} = A \\
& A.\overline{A} = 0 & & A+\overline{A} = 1 &
\end{array}$$

(b) For gates or combinations of gates with inputs A, B and C

$$\begin{array}{ll}
\text{AND} \quad A.B = B.A & \text{OR} \quad A+B = B+A \\
(A.B).C = A.(B.C) & (A+B)+C = A+(B+C) \\
(A+B).(A+C) = A+(B.C) & (A.B)+(A.C) = A.(B+C)
\end{array}$$

(c) De Morgan's theorem, which formulates the relationship between (N)AND and (N)OR functions:

$$\overline{A.B} = \overline{A}+\overline{B} \qquad\qquad\qquad \overline{A+B} = \overline{A}.\overline{B}$$
$$A.B = \overline{\overline{A}+\overline{B}} \qquad\qquad\qquad A+B = \overline{\overline{A}.\overline{B}}$$

Verify the last line of section (b) above using ICs. A quad two-input AND gate and a quad two-input OR gate are needed for each of these identities. **7408, 7432** **4081, 4071** Figure 2.2 shows the circuits for one of them. LEDs should be connected to indicate the states of the inputs and output as in chapter 1.

De Morgan's theorem is a very powerful tool when analysing logic functions: *to*

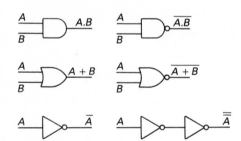

Figure 2.1   Gate symbols and Boolean notation

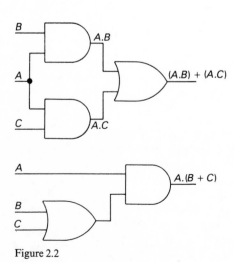

Figure 2.2

Questions

1 Write out a truth table with 8 rows and 8 columns of A, B, C, $A.B$, $A.C$, $A.B+A.C$, $B+C$ and $A.(B+C)$ to check that

$(A.B)+(A.C) = A.(B+C)$

2 Show that

$(A+B).(A+C) = A+(B.C)$

by multiplying out the left-hand side and using the identities from section (a) above.

3 Check figure 2.3 using truth tables.

obtain the inverse of a Boolean function, invert each variable and exchange 'AND' for 'OR'. To find the inverse of the OR function, $A + B$, invert each variable and exchange 'AND' for 'OR' (. for +). Thus we can write

$$\overline{A+B} = \bar{A}.\bar{B}$$

'NOT(A OR B)' is identical to '(NOT A) AND (NOT B)'.

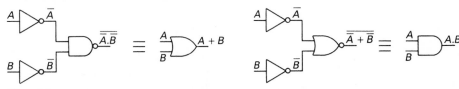

Figure 2.3

By looking at figure 2.3 you can see that the tasks in section 1.5 were just examples to justify de Morgan's theorem. The theorem states how the OR gate can be made from a NAND gate and two NOT gates.

De Morgan's theorem is not only useful in the simplification of logic expressions, but also for the conversion of a system entirely to NAND or NOR gates. This is sometimes necessary if the logic system is to be made in the form of a single integrated circuit, as it is simpler to manufacture circuits like this, even though more gates may be necessary.

A	B	Y
0	0	0
0	1	1
1	0	1
1	1	0

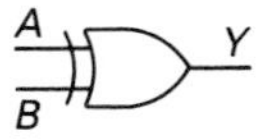

Figure 2.4 The exclusive OR gate

2.3 The exclusive OR gate

The OR gate of section 1.5 includes the condition, *if $A = 1$ and $B = 1$, then $Y = 1$.* Another useful logic gate, called the *exclusive OR* or *anticoincidence* gate (written EOR or XOR) has $Y = 0$ for this input condition. Its truth table and symbol are shown in figure 2.4. You should be able to see that the output is '(A AND (NOT B)) OR ((NOT A) AND B)'. In Boolean notation, this is written

$$Y = A.\bar{B} + \bar{A}.B$$

or in even shorter notation,

$$Y = A \oplus B$$

The gate can be constructed in several ways. Following the expression above, figure 2.5 shows the required arrangement of two-input gates. Construct this circuit and check that it gives the required logic. 7404, 7408, 7432 4069, 4081, 4071

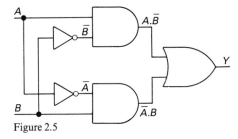

Figure 2.5

Questions

4 Write down the truth table for the parity gate.

5 Write in words a summary of the truth table. Write the summary in Boolean algebra.

6 Draw the logic diagram.

The *coincidence, parity* or *exclusive NOR* gate is the inverse or *complement* of the EOR gate. Another NOT gate can be added to the output of the circuit in figure 2.5 to produce the parity gate. Instead of doing this, rearrange the NOT gates at the inputs to construct a parity gate. Only two input leads need to be altered. Check that the new circuit gives the required logic.

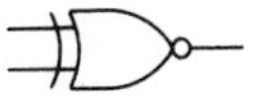

Figure 2.6 The exclusive NOR gate

2.4 Exercises in circuit analysis

Boolean analysis is not necessary for solving simple problems. It is included here because it is a useful mathematical technique, but you may prefer just to use truth tables. Make a note of the logic diagrams in figures 2.7 and 2.8, though, even if you do not follow the algebra. They are all useful.

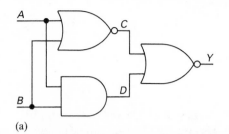

Figure 2.7   Examples of the exclusive OR gate

(a)

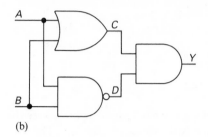

(b)

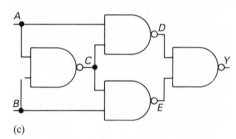

(c)

A Boolean expression for the output of figure 2.7(a) is

$$Y = \overline{(\overline{A+B})+(A.B)}$$

Using de Morgan's theorem,

$$Y = (\overline{\overline{A+B}}).(\overline{A.B}) = (A+B).(\overline{A.B})$$

Using de Morgan's theorem to expand the second set of brackets,

$$Y = (A+B).(\overline{A}+\overline{B})$$

Multiplying out the brackets,

$$Y = A.\overline{A}+A.\overline{B}+B.\overline{A}+B.\overline{B}$$

From the rule table of section 2.2, $A.\overline{A} = B.\overline{B} = 0$, so

$$Y = A.\overline{B}+\overline{A}.B$$

which is the basic statement for the EOR gate.

Construct the circuit and check its function. **7408, 7402** **4081, 4001**

Write down truth tables for the logic diagrams in figures 2.7(c) and 2.8, to check that they act as labelled. These both have the advantage over other methods of making the same gate using NAND or NOR gates only, that they require only four gates, which are housed on one IC.

It is useful to be able to make any given combination of functions from an arrangement of one type of gate. This often simplifies the circuit and reduces the number of ICs required. Consider the simple example of figure 2.9(a). The output is '(A OR B) AND (NOT C)'. This can be constructed from just two NOR gates, as shown in figure 2.9(b).

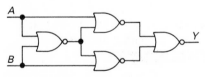

Figure 2.8   The exclusive NOR gate

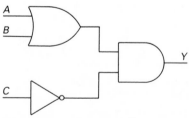
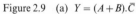

Figure 2.9   (a) $Y = (A+B).\overline{C}$

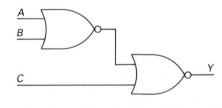

(b) $Y = (A+B).\overline{C}$

To solve any given problem, the best method is first to write down a Boolean expression or a truth table for the output. As an example of this approach, consider a voting system for three people that is to be designed such that indicator 1 lights for a majority *in favour* and indicator 2 lights for a majority *against*. The Boolean expression for the output (indicator 1) is

$$Y = A.B+B.C+C.A$$

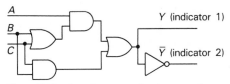

Figure 2.10   A voting system for three people

Using the rules given in section 2.2, this can be written as

$$Y = A.(B+C)+B.C$$

A logic diagram for $A.(B+C)$ was shown in figure 2.2, so the complete solution of the problem is as shown in figure 2.10.

Construct this circuit to see if it works satisfactorily, using only two ICs (i.e. use one quad NOR gate instead of the two OR gates). `7408, 7402` `4081, 4001`

2.5   Binary arithmetic

A	B	SUM	CARRY
0	0	0	0
0	1	1	0
1	0	1	0
1	1	0	1

Figure 2.11   The half adder

Binary arithmetic only needs two digits, 0 and 1. Figure 3.19 on page 23 shows how denary (ordinary) numbers convert into binary ones. The truth table for the addition of two binary digits or *bits*, A and B, is shown in figure 2.11. Looking at the *sum bit* and the *carry bit* as outputs from two separate systems, the sum bit can be found from

$$SUM = A \oplus B$$

and the carry bit from

$$CARRY = A.B$$

Any of the logic diagrams in figure 2.12 will give the required truth table.

Construct one circuit from figure 2.12 and check that it behaves as expected. `7400, 7402, 7404, 7408, 7432` `4011, 4001, 4069, 4081, 4071` This circuit is called a *half adder*. By using the same circuit but with different connections, it can be converted into a *half subtractor*, to produce $A-B$. Look at the truth table for the half subtractor in figure 2.13, then make the necessary adjustment to your adder circuit and check that it functions correctly.

Figure 2.12   Half adder circuits

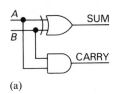

(a)

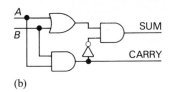

(b)

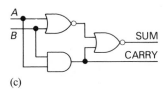

(c)

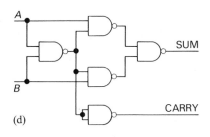

(d)

A	B	DIFFERENCE	BORROW
0	0	0	0
0	1	1	1
1	0	1	0
1	1	0	0

Figure 2.13   Truth table for the half subtractor

For complete binary addition a *full adder* is required, in order to accept the *carry bit* from the previous stage (see figure 2.14). Write down the truth table for the full adder, construct the circuit and check that it performs the required function (see figure 2.15). This is an elaborate circuit, requiring a large number of ICs and interconnecting leads, so you may prefer to miss this exercise out and proceed to the next, where four full adders are contained in one package.

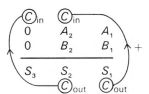

Figure 2.14   The addition operation

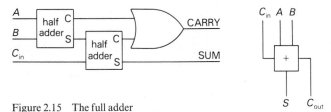

Figure 2.15   The full adder

Questions

12 Write down Boolean expressions for the outputs and draw the block diagram for a half subtractor.

13 Add 11 to 01 to show how the *carry in* (C_{in}) is used in the addition of A_2 and B_2.

A single 4-bit binary full adder can be used for parallel addition, subtraction and multiplication. Serial division is described in sections 3.6 and 7.2, and serial addition in section 7.3. Schematically, the 4-bit full adder IC appears as in figure 2.16.

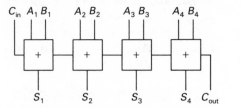

Figure 2.16   4-bit addition

Set up two numbers using the TTL 74283 or CMOS 4008 IC and display the sum using the four-LED indicator. **74283, I** **4008, I** Remember to connect all unused inputs to 0 V. One extra indicator will be needed if the sum is greater than 15 (1111 in binary).

Full subtraction can be performed by a 4-bit adder, by using a mathematical property of binary numbers. The block diagram is shown in figure 2.17. Note that C_{out} is fed back as the carry in C_{in}. If $B > A$, then to form $B - A$, add B and $\bar{A}$, and the sum S will be the answer. This can be written as the following equation:

$$S = B - A = (B + \bar{A} + 1) - 10000$$

If $B < A$, then the answer will be $\bar{S}$. Use the 4-bit adder IC and a hex inverter IC to check that the *recipe* above gives the right answers. **74283, 7404, I** **4008, 4069, I**

Four AND gates and two half adders are needed to multiply two numbers $A_2 A_1$ and $B_2 B_1$ (figure 2.18). Use part of the 4-bit adder IC and a quad AND gate IC to construct a multiplier. **74283, 7408, I** **4008, 4081, I**

Questions

14 Perform the operation in figure 2.17 on paper to show that $9 - 4 = 5$. Note that $\bar{A} = 1011$, and do not forget that $C_{in} = 1$ since $C_{out} = 1$.

15 Show that

$$A_2 A_1 \times B_2 B_1 = S_4 S_3 S_2 S_1$$

(e.g. $10 \times 11 = 0110$), as shown in figure 2.18.

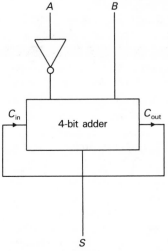

Figure 2.17   Subtraction

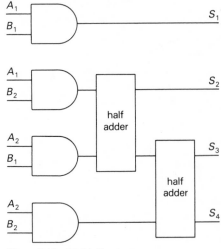

Figure 2.18   Multiplication

2.6   Further questions

1 Make $A + B.C$ from three two-input NAND gates.

2 'A OR B AND C' can mean 'A OR (B AND C)' or '(A OR B) AND C'. Write out an eight-column truth table for each of these expressions. Compare them to find the values of A, B and C for which they are different.

3 Show that an EOR gate can be used as a *controlled inverter*, which operates so that if input $A = 1$, output $Y = $ input $\bar{B}$ and if $A = 0$, $Y = B$. (By connecting a quad EOR gate to the A inputs of a 4-bit adder, the adder can be used as an adder or as a subtractor by using this control function. The carry in and carry out connections of the adder have to be altered too.)

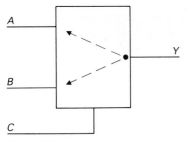

Figure 2.19

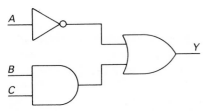

Figure 2.20

A	B	Bo$_{in}$	D	Bo$_{out}$
1	1	1	1	1
1	0	1	0	0
0	1	1	0	1
0	0	1	1	1
1	1	0	0	0
1	0	0	1	0
0	1	0	1	1
0	0	0	0	0

Figure 2.21

4 Figure 2.12(d) shows a half adder made only of NAND gates. Design a similar circuit using only NOR gates.

5 The electronic switch or *2-to-1 line multiplexer* shown in figure 2.19 has output $Y = A.\bar{C} + B.C$ (i.e. $Y = A$ if $C = 0$). Design such a circuit using AND, NOT and OR gates. Simplify the circuit to four NAND gates.

6 (a) Write down a Boolean expression for the output of figure 2.20.
   (b) Convert each gate into a combination of NAND gates and reduce the logic diagram to a minimum number of gates.
   (c) Write down a Boolean expression for the output of the NAND gate logic diagram in (b).
   (d) Use de Morgan's theorem to show that the Boolean expressions in (a) and (c) are equivalent.

7 (Hard) Section 2.5 contained circuits for a full adder and a half subtractor. Design a circuit for a *full subtractor*. It has three inputs – A, B and *borrow in* (Bo_{in}) – and two outputs – *difference* and *borrow out* (Bo_{out}). The truth table of figure 2.21 has to be studied carefully to appreciate how the subtractor works. However, to design the circuit, it is only necessary to implement the table in gates.

8 Design a *binary–decimal decoder* for a 2-bit binary number A_2A_1. The truth table for this device is shown in figure 2.22.

A$_2$	A$_1$	Y$_1$	Y$_2$	Y$_3$	Y$_4$
0	0	1	0	0	0
0	1	0	1	0	0
1	0	0	0	1	0
1	1	0	0	0	1

Figure 2.22

9 Design a *decimal–binary encoder*, i.e. a circuit with three inputs (for numbers 1, 2 and 3) and two outputs that will produce the equivalent 2-bit binary number. Construct the required truth table or write Boolean expressions for the two outputs. The output 00 should be produced by having all three inputs at logic 0.

10 Two 1-bit binary numbers A and B are to be compared. Design a circuit with three outputs X, Y and Z, where $X = 1$ if $A > B$, $Y = 1$ if $A = B$ and $Z = 1$ if $A < B$.

11 A circuit which compares numbers is called a *comparator*.
   (a) Design a 2-bit binary number comparator, using two exclusive NOR gates and one simple logic gate, to give an output $Y = 1$ only if the two numbers A_2A_1 and B_2B_1 are equal, i.e. if $A_2A_1 = B_2B_1$.
   (b) (Hard) Design a comparator to produce an output $Y = 1$ if $A_2A_1 > B_2B_1$.

12 Design a voting system for four people to light an indicator for a majority in favour, using two-input gates.

13 Use Boolean algebra to show that the logic diagrams in figures 1.20(a), (b) and (c) are three-input NOR, AND and NAND gates, respectively.

14 (a) Write down Boolean expressions for points C, D, E and Y in figure 2.7(c) in terms of A and B. Use the rules of Boolean algebra to simplify your expression to

$$Y = A.\bar{B} + \bar{A}.B$$

   (b) Show that

$$\overline{A.\bar{B} + \bar{A}.B} = A.B + \bar{A}.\bar{B}$$

   (These are two expressions for the output of the exclusive NOR or parity gate, the construction of which is described in section 2.3.)

3 Sequential logic

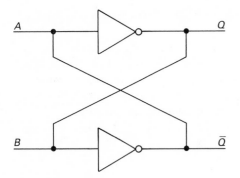

Figure 3.1   The simple bistable

Questions

1 What happens when both A and B are connected to the V^+ rail (logic 1) together? (*Do not leave the connections like this for more than a few seconds.*)
2 What happens if B is touched to logic 1 when $Q = 1$?

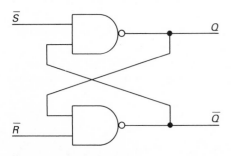

Figure 3.2   The $\bar{S}\bar{R}$ bistable

Question

3 What will happen if both $\bar{S}$ and $\bar{R}$ are set to 0 V? Try it.

3.1   Introduction

In the combinational logic circuits of chapter 2, the outputs labelled Y depended *only* on the logic states of the inputs A, B, etc., *at the same instant of time*. The sequential logic circuits of this chapter have outputs, which will be labelled Q and $\bar{Q}$, that are determined not only by the logic states of the inputs but also by the previous values of the inputs (i.e. the outputs may depend on time). Some of the circuits can store digital information and thus are said to have *memory*. The simplest circuit is the *bistable* or *latch*, which is made from two NOT gates.

3.2   Simple bistable – a 1-bit memory cell

Set up the cross-coupled NOT gate circuit (figure 3.1) with the two outputs Q and $\bar{Q}$ coupled to two LED indicators. `7404` `4069` With both inputs floating (i.e. not connected to the V^+ or the 0 V rail), one LED will be on and the other off. Q and $\bar{Q}$ are used as symbols for the outputs because the outputs are in opposite logic states. If $Q = 1$, connect input A to logic 1 (the V^+ rail) *momentarily*. If $\bar{Q} = 1$, connect input B to logic 1 *momentarily*. The outputs will switch. (You may have noticed that you are breaking the rule given at the end of section 1.4 by making the double connection, but it is only for an instant.)

This circuit needs modifying for it to work in system 3 (see section 1.3). It will function as described if Q and $\bar{Q}$ are each connected to transistor amplifiers (see figure 1.16) to act as indicators. The 1 kΩ resistor in the circuit in figure 1.16 should be replaced by a 100 Ω resistor in series with an LED.

The output of each gate is fed back to the input of the other, so both gates are *latched*, or held in a particular logic state, when the input connections are floating. Therefore the system has two stable states: $Q = 1$, $\bar{Q} = 0$ and $Q = 0$, $\bar{Q} = 1$. This is an example of *positive feedback*, in which any change at the output causes the input to *increase* the change at the output. This means that the switch between the stable states is made very rapidly.

The astable circuit which you will study in section 3.7 is another example of a system using positive feedback.

3.3   The *SR* bistable

The bistable in figure 3.1 can be made from NAND gates with both inputs connected together. `7400` `4011` An alternative method of connection is shown in figure 3.2. This allows logic pulses rather than mechanical switches to alter the output states. Set up the circuit and connect $\bar{S}$ and $\bar{R}$ to logic 1. Follow through the pulse sequence (timing diagram) given in figure 3.3 and check the truth table in figure 3.4. Note that either Q or $\bar{Q}$ can be at logic 1 at the beginning of the sequence, with the other at logic 0.

When $\bar{S} = \bar{R} = 1$, the positive feedback from the output holds the circuit in its last switched state. The negative pulse to $\bar{S}$ *writes* or *sets* a '1' into the memory cell. Q must go to logic 1 and $\bar{Q}$ to logic 0. The negative pulse to $\bar{R}$ *resets* the Q output to '0'.

The Q output of the circuit also acts as a *debounced switch* or latch. With the switch at $\bar{R}$ (figure 3.5), the first negative pulse to $\bar{S}$ switches Q to 1. Further pulses to $\bar{S}$ have

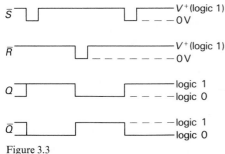

Figure 3.3

$\bar{S}$	$\bar{R}$	Q	$\bar{Q}$
1	1	1 or 0	0 or 1
0	1	1	0
1	0	0	1

Figure 3.4

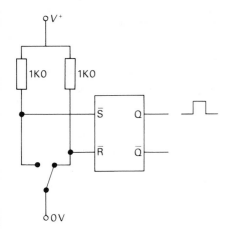

Figure 3.5   The debounced switch **S**

no effect until the switch is reset to $\bar{R}$. An input switch with a voltage–time trace like that in figure 3.6 (a chattering switch) will cause only one transition at output Q, hence the name of the circuit.

The debounced switch (figure 3.5) is essential for producing individual clock pulses for the circuits to be constructed in the rest of this chapter. This circuit will be signified by the symbol **S**. Make one and keep it connected on the end of the breadboard. To indicate when the switch is at logic 1, *either* replace the left 1 kΩ resistor by an LED and safety resistor *or* connect the indicator between $\bar{Q}$ and the V^+ rail.

The $\bar{S}$ and $\bar{R}$ notation that has been used here for inputs (and that will be used elsewhere for preset and clear) needs to be explained. When the input changes from logic 1 to logic 0 to alter the output of the circuit, the input will have a *bar* over it. Such inputs are said to be *active low*. When the change is from logic 0 to logic 1 for the output to alter, there will be no bar. This is why the next circuit uses the symbols S and R rather than $\bar{S}$ and $\bar{R}$.

Add two further NAND gates to the inputs of figure 3.2 to function as NOT gates (see figure 3.7). This is the *SR bistable*. The pulse sequence of figure 3.3 is inverted, and the output states of the bistable are now changed by the *rising* or *leading edge* of each pulse. The states of the outputs are shown in figure 3.8.

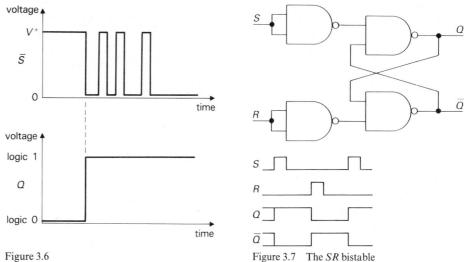

Figure 3.6   Figure 3.7   The *SR* bistable

S	R	Q	$\bar{Q}$
0	0	1 or 0	0 or 1
1	0	1	0
0	1	0	1

Figure 3.8   The *SR* bistable

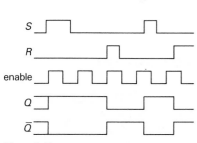

Figure 3.10

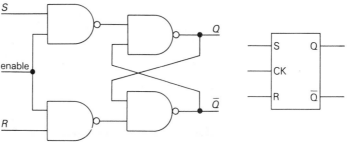

Figure 3.9   The *SR* flip-flop

The second input on each of the inverting NAND gates can be used as an *enable* (see figure 3.9). Only when this enable input is high (logic 1) can the bistable inputs change the outputs (see figure 3.10). By using a single *master pulse generator* or clock

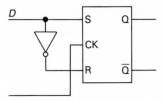

Figure 3.11

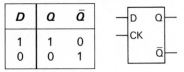

D	S	R	Q	$\bar{Q}$
0	0	1	0	1
1	1	0	1	0

Figure 3.12

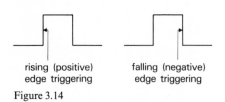

D	Q	$\bar{Q}$
1	1	0
0	0	1

Figure 3.13   The D flip-flop

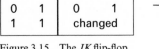

rising (positive)   falling (negative)
edge triggering   edge triggering

Figure 3.14

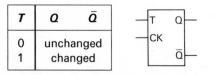

J	K	Q	$\bar{Q}$
0	0	unchanged	
1	0	1	0
0	1	0	1
1	1	changed	

Figure 3.15   The JK flip-flop

T	Q	$\bar{Q}$
0	unchanged	
1	changed	

Figure 3.16   The T flip-flop

connected to the enable inputs of all the bistables in a large system, the information that is passed to each bistable input is also passed to the corresponding output at the same moment. This reduces the risk of information passing through a system in the wrong order – a possibility called the *race hazard*.

Clocked bistables are called *flip-flops*. In each of the tables relating the outputs of the SR and $\overline{SR}$ bistables to their input states, one row has been deliberately omitted. For the input state $S = R = 1$ for the SR bistable, both Q and $\bar{Q}$ are logic 1. When you try to switch both S and R simultaneously from 1 to 0, it is not possible to predict which of Q or $\bar{Q}$ will change to 0 and which will remain at logic 1. This *indeterminate* condition should never be allowed to arise. It is avoided by using modified SR flip-flops called the D flip-flop and the JK flip-flop.

3.4   The *D* flip-flop

Add an inverter across the S and R inputs of figure 3.9 to produce the circuit shown in figure 3.11. `7400, 7404` `4011, 4069` The states of the outputs after the rising edge (0 to 1) of the clock pulse are shown in figure 3.12. This is the D flip-flop (see figure 3.13). Notice that the logic state at the D input is transferred to the Q output on the rising edge of each clock pulse, whatever the logic state of the Q output was before the clock pulse. This information is stored until the rising edge of the next clock pulse. Such a device is called a *data latch* (see section 7.2).

The SR and D flip-flops both change their output states whilst the clock input is high. If two bits of data arrive at the D input during a clock pulse, the first will be lost. This can be avoided by making the clock pulses very short. A better method is to use a sequence of flip-flops in what is called a *master–slave* arrangement. In this arrangement the output is determined by the input logic state at a chosen instant during the clock pulse. This instant is either the rising (positive) edge or the falling (negative) edge of the pulse (see figure 3.14). The pin-out charts in appendix I indicate the edge triggering of the different ICs used in this book. The way that flip-flops are connected together to make devices like counters will depend on whether the flip-flops trigger on the rising or the falling edge of the clock pulse, as you will see in section 3.6.

3.5   The *JK* flip-flop

Set up one JK flip-flop (see figure 3.15). `7476` `4027` (There are two in each IC.) Note that the power supply connections for TTL 7476 are in an unusual position. Remember also that for *simple* experiments it is usually safe to leave any inputs that are to be at logic 1 floating for TTL ICs. This often drastically reduces the number of wires on a breadboard. For CMOS 4027 do not forget to ground (connect to 0 V) all unused inputs. (This will include pins 4, 7, 9 and 12.)

Connect J and K to either logic 0 or logic 1. Observe the result of a clock pulse on the outputs Q and $\bar{Q}$ (see figure 3.15). `S` With CMOS 4027, the outputs will only change on the rising edge of the pulse; with TTL 7476 they will change on the falling edge. When J and K are different, the flip-flop behaves as a D type, and J acts as the D input. When $J = K = 1$, the outputs switch or *toggle*. This arrangement is called a T flip-flop (see figure 3.16). You will see how to connect the D flip-flop to behave as a T type in section 3.6.

3.6   The asynchronous or ripple counter

Set up a JK flip-flop as a T flip-flop by making $J = K = 1$. `7476, S` `4027, S` Note that $Q = 1$ for every other clock pulse. The flip-flop is dividing the number of input clock pulses by two. In figure 3.17, Q_A pulses at half the frequency of the clock, Q_B at half that of Q_A, etc. (see figure 3.18).

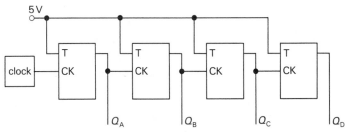

Figure 3.17   A 4-bit binary up-counter (falling-edge triggered)

denary (pulse number)	binary			
	Q_D	Q_C	Q_B	Q_A
0	0	0	0	0
1	0	0	0	1
2	0	0	1	0
3	0	0	1	1
4	0	1	0	0
5	0	1	0	1
6	0	1	1	0
7	0	1	1	1
8	1	0	0	0

Figure 3.19

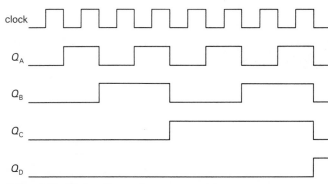

Figure 3.18   Timing diagram for an up-counter

Connect four flip-flops as in figure 3.17 to produce the 4-bit binary up-counter, which counts 1, 2, 3, etc. in binary (see figure 3.19). **S, 2 × 7476, I** **S, 2 × 4027, 4069, I** Connect the four outputs Q_A to Q_D to the four-LED indicator IC of section 1.4. The clock pulse must come from a debounced switch. Observe how the output display appears to change randomly when a mechanical switch or a flying lead is used at the clock input. Random counts sometimes still occur even with the debounced switch. This is most likely if you are using low-power Schottky TTL chips.* Connect a capacitor or two of between 0.01 and 0.1 μF across the power rails between the ICs. This should cure the problem. Another method to try to suppress unexpected spurious counts is to connect low-value capacitors between the IC inputs and ground (the 0 V rail).

For the leading-edge triggered CMOS 4027, $\bar{Q}_A$ (not Q_A) must be connected to the next clock input to produce an up-counter. The clock pulses must also be inverted to obtain the diagram of figure 3.18. Remember to connect pins 4, 7, 9 and 12 to ground. These pins are the *set* (or *preset*) and *reset* (or *clear*). Pins 2, 3, 7 and 8 on TTL 7476 are the equivalent. They can be left unconnected, i.e. floating at logic 1.

Observe the effect of putting the preset or clear (never both together) to logic 0 for TTL 7476 or to logic 1 for CMOS 4027. These are called *direct inputs* and over-ride any effects caused by the clock. Using the direct inputs and one or more logic gates, a counter can be constructed which will reset at any chosen number to any other number. Notice that bars have been placed over the headings preset and clear in the table for TTL 7476 in appendix I, to indicate that these inputs are *active low*, i.e. at logic 0 not logic 1.

Questions

4 Continue figure 3.19 for a 4-bit binary counter to count to pulse 15.
5 What happens if $\bar{Q}$, not Q, is connected into the clock input of the next flip-flop in figure 3.17?
6 Invert the clock pulse too. Draw a timing diagram similar to the one in figure 3.18 for the circuit in question **5**.
7 How can the counter be used as a divide-by-four or divide-by-eight circuit?
8 How can the TTL 7476 counter be reset at 10 with an OR gate? (Or how can the CMOS 4027 counter be reset with a NOR gate?) Try it to see if your answer works. (Hint· use the $\bar{Q}$ outputs.)
9 How can the counter be used as a die, i.e. to reset at 7 to show 1? (A three-input gate is needed.)

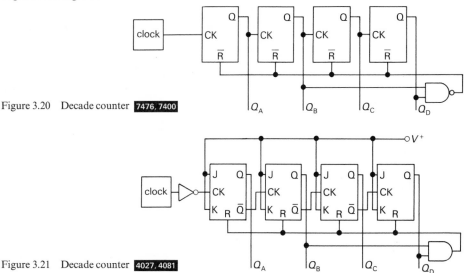

Figure 3.20   Decade counter **7476, 7400**

Figure 3.21   Decade counter **4027, 4081**

Construct a decade counter (figure 3.20 or 3.21). **÷7400** **÷4081** It is possible to divide by 3, 5, 6, 10 or 12 using this circuit, by connecting the two inputs to the

* These are slightly faster than normal TTL chips and use only one-fifth of the power.

resetting gate to different pairs of Q outputs. The number of output states the counter goes through before being reset to zero is called the *modulo* of the counter.

To make the clock to the counter automatic, use one of the pulse-producing circuits from section 3.7 in place of the debounced switch. You can then observe the timing diagram shown in figure 3.18 at each input or output of the counter by using an oscilloscope. Connect the clock output to the external trigger input of the oscilloscope and to the Y-input. Adjust the horizontal position of the trace so that the rising edge of the clock pulse is in line with the left-hand edge of the graticule. Adjust the oscilloscope time base to make each pulse about 1 cm wide. Next connect outputs Q_A to Q_D to the Y-input in turn, and note how the outputs change relative to the initial clock timing pattern. You may need to readjust the time base setting while doing this. You must interpret what you see carefully, because two stationary pulse patterns are possible for each output. Which you will see depends on which clock pulse it is that triggers the oscilloscope. Check which one is correct by looking at figure 3.18.

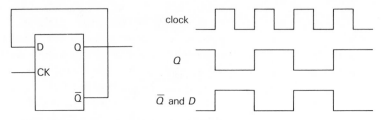

Figure 3.22   A D flip-flop connected as a T flip-flop

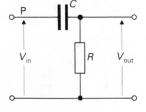

Figure 3.23

Question

10 What is the result of omitting the NOT gate from the circuit of figure 3.23? Would the circuit still count?

The D flip-flop can be connected to perform as a T flip-flop (see figure 3.22). Connect two D flip-flops as in figure 3.23 to make a 2-bit binary up-counter.
S, 7474, 7404, I **S, 4013, 4069, I** Each clock pulse transfers the D input to the Q output. $\bar{Q}$ is then fed back to D for the next clock pulse. Output Q switches logic states at each clock pulse. Notice that the clock connections are the same as for the CMOS circuit of figure 3.21. This is because both flip-flops trigger on the rising edge. The down-counter (i.e. counts 3, 2, 1, 0) is made by omitting the NOT gate and connecting Q_A, not $\bar{Q}_A$, to the next clock input. If you have done question **5** above, you will have seen that the up-counter must be falling-edge triggered. A rising-edge triggered counter will behave as a down-counter if connected as in figure 3.17.

3.7 Pulse producers – the astable and monostable

Making spikes

Connect together a 1 kΩ resistor and a 0.1 μF capacitor to make the small RC combination shown in figure 3.24. Connect an oscilloscope across V_{out}. With correct adjustment of the controls, you can see the voltage–time trace shown when a flying lead at P is moved from 0 V to V^+ and then back to 0 V. A positive spike is produced

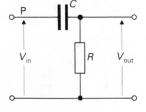

Figure 3.24

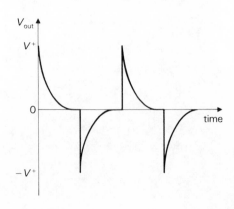

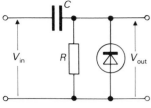

Figure 3.25

Figure 3.26

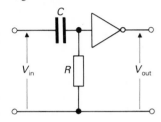

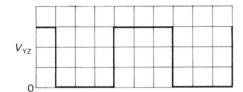

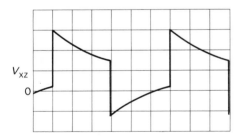

Figure 3.27

for a transition from logic 0 to logic 1 and a negative spike for a transition from logic 1 to logic 0. By adding a diode in parallel (see figure 3.25) with the resistor, you can suppress the negative spikes. If you want a short pulse for a transition from logic 1 to 0 and back to 1, then the circuit in figure 3.26 can be used. For $R = 1\,\text{k}\Omega$ and $C = 0.1\,\mu\text{F}$, the pulse lasts less than 0.5 ms. The pulse height falls from its peak value to 0.37 of this value in a time RC seconds, and to zero in about $5RC$ seconds, where R is measured in ohms and C in farads. A series of spikes can be produced if any of these circuits is connected to a clock output which is emitting square pulses. You will find an explanation of the physics of pulsed RC circuits in most A level physics textbooks, if you are interested in the theory.

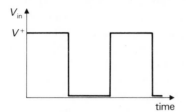
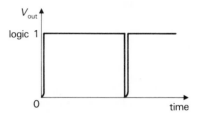

The astable

When the value of RC in figure 3.24 is not small in comparison to the width of the input pulse V_{in}, the oscilloscope trace of the output will look like V_{XZ} in figure 3.27. Adding a NOT gate between the oscilloscope and the output to produce the circuit of figure 3.26 will give you an oscilloscope trace that looks like V_{YZ}. If this square pulse is used as the clock pulse to an identical circuit, the output of which is fed back positively to the input of the first circuit, the *astable* circuit (figure 3.28) is produced. The system should be self starting.

Set up the circuit in figure 3.28. `7404, I` `4069, I` Use an oscilloscope to observe the waveforms V_{XZ} and V_{YZ}. Vary the values of R and C to see how the combination affects the pulse rate. With slow pulse rates, you will see the LEDs flashing alternately. For system 3, you will need to use two transistors, as described in section 3.2. The voltage–time graphs shown in figure 3.27 are for TTL chips. The CMOS ones look a little different. The CMOS astable is often difficult to start. If it does not start, use a larger resistor and smaller capacitor. You may find that the circuits in figures 3.32(a) and (b) are easier to use with CMOS chips. For TTL gates, make sure that $R \leqslant 1\,\text{k}\Omega$, or the circuit will not function. Figure 3.28 can be redrawn in a similar way to the other flip-flop circuits, as shown in figure 3.29. You can use either Q or $\bar{Q}$ to provide clock pulses for the counter or shift register circuits.

The astable circuit can also be made from NOR gates (see figure 3.30) `7402, I` `4001, I` or from NAND gates. One input to one gate can be used as an enable (see section 1.7) to switch the astable on or off as required. The input to the lower TTL NOR gate in figure 3.30 floats at logic 1 until S is closed, enabling the circuit.

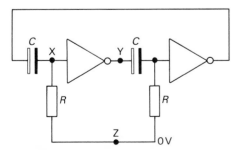

Figure 3.28   The simple astable

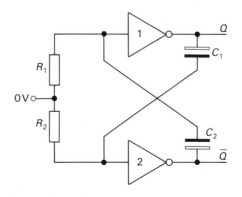

Figure 3.29   The simple astable

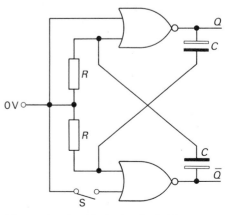

Figure 3.30   Astable circuit using NOR gates

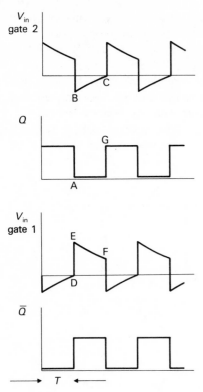

Figure 3.31   Action of the astable circuit in Figure 3.29

The next paragraph explains the action of the TTL astable circuit. It is difficult to follow, but is included here as an example of a typical circuit analysis.

The duration T of the astable pulse depends on the potential difference at which a gate switches off. T is approximately equal to RC, so the frequency of the astable is roughly equal to $1/(2RC)$. When the output Q is pulled low (point A in figure 3.31), the capacitor C_1 connected to it is charged. The input to gate 2 is pulled negative because the p.d. across the capacitor cannot change instantaneously (point B). Thus $\bar{Q}$ goes high. C_1 starts to discharge back to 0 V (point C). The other capacitor C_2 is initially uncharged (point D). The p.d. across it also cannot change suddenly, so the input to gate 1 is pulled high with $\bar{Q}$ (point E). As C_2 charges through R_1, the p.d. across R_1 falls, since the sum of the p.d.s across R_1 and C_2 is constant. The input p.d. to gate 1 falls to the logic 0 threshold (point F). This threshold is 1.5 V for TTL (see figure 1.14). So gate 1 switches and Q goes high (point G). C_1 has just discharged (point C). Thus the input to gate 2 is pulled high, which pulls $\bar{Q}$ low. C_2 starts to discharge and C_1 to charge through R_1, etc.

Figure 3.32 shows three other useful square-wave generator circuits. The 555 timer of section 8.3 is a most useful and versatile square-wave generator too. You may like to experiment with some of these circuits to find out over what ranges they oscillate satisfactorily and just what shape and how long their output pulses are.

Figure 3.32   Square-wave generators

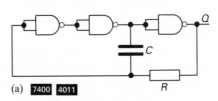

(a) `7400` `4011`

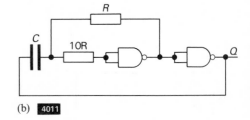

(b) `4011`

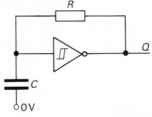

(c) The Schmitt trigger `7414` `40106`

The monostable

A monostable circuit is used to produce a *single* square output pulse. Make the circuit in figure 3.33 using two NAND gates. `7400, I` `4011, I` If you are using TTL, then for a one-second pulse you will have to use a very large capacitor. R must be no greater than 1 kΩ so C has to be at least 1000 μF. An advantage of using CMOS is that you can use a very large R and a small C to produce the same pulse. Connect point A from V^+ to 0 V. The output pulse $\bar{Q}$ is always the same length, whatever the length of the input pulse. Notice that the monostable is triggered by the falling edge of a pulse. You can observe the pulse shapes using an oscilloscope. For system 3, you will need to use two transistors as described in section 3.2 rather than simple LED indicators.

The 555 timer can be connected to act as a monostable too (see section 8.3).

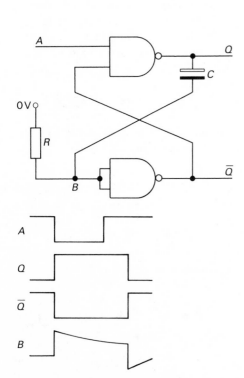

Figure 3.33   The monostable circuit

> ### Question
>
> **11** Explain why the NAND gate circuit in figure 3.33 always has an output pulse of constant length at $\bar{Q}$.

3.8 Further questions

1 The pairs of pulses shown in figure 3.34(a) and (b) are fed to the inputs of (i) an AND, (ii) a NAND and (iii) a NOR gate. Sketch the output pulse from each gate for each pair of input pulses.

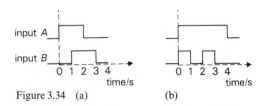

Figure 3.34 (a)   (b)

2 Show that the circuit of figure 3.35 is an *SR* flip-flop.

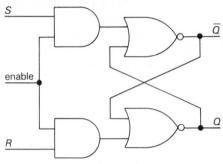

Figure 3.35

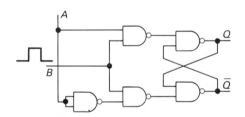

Figure 3.36

3 In figure 3.36, what is the effect on the outputs Q and $\bar{Q}$ of a clock pulse at B (a) when A is at logic 1 and (b) when A is at logic 0? What is this circuit?

4 Modify figure 3.20 so that the counter counts down from 9 to 0 and can be reset to 9. (The reset is a difficult problem.)

5 (a) How many flip-flops are needed to build counters that will reset after 7, 15 and 31?

(b) Write an equation which relates the maximum count capacity to the number of flip-flops required.

6 Design a circuit with two pulsed outputs, one an octave above the other (i.e. twice its frequency).

7 Design a circuit using an asynchronous counter which will divide by 9.

8 (a) Use an astable, a counter and an AND gate to make a circuit that makes eight equal pulses and then stops. How do you start this circuit?

(b) Modify the circuit by omitting the AND gate and using the enable function on the astable instead.

(c) Use an astable and a monostable to make a circuit with the same function. What is the advantage, if any, of the counter circuit over this one?

9 Change and add to the circuit of figure 1.19 so that it will act as a burglar alarm. A warning note is to sound when the LDR is illuminated by a light being switched on.

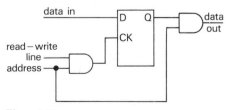

Figure 3.37

10 A RAM (*random access memory*) is an array of 1-bit read/write cells such as the one in figure 3.37. A particular cell or row of cells is chosen by its address. One bit can be written or read in each cell when the address or clock is high. Explain (a) how the read–write line operates and (b) the action to store and retrieve data from the cell. Does the cell retain its information once it has been read? Modify the circuit so that the read facility is disabled when writing.

4 Analogue systems

4.1 Introduction

Analogue electronic systems process electrical signals which vary continuously with time, unlike digital systems, whose signals are discrete pulses. An example of an analogue system is a disc record player: the plastic disc contains a wavy groove which is a mechanical analogue of the original sound wave. The 'wiggles' in the groove are detected and amplified by a pick-up and amplifier and fed to a loudspeaker (an analogue transducer), which converts the information into sound waves.

The electronic link in this chain is the amplifier, and linear amplifiers are at the heart of most analogue systems. They are called *linear* because the output signal is directly proportional to the input signal, and *amplifiers* because the electrical power delivered from the output is greater than the electrical power absorbed by the input. Therefore, an amplifier will only work when it is connected to a suitable power supply – not even electronics is allowed to contravene the conservation of energy!

A study of electronic analogue systems starts with the operational amplifier, which is the fundamental building block for many systems, including control systems, audio, radio and television systems, servos and analogue computers.

4.2 The operational amplifier

The operational amplifier, or *op-amp*, is an amplifier with a very large *gain*. That is, when the voltage between the input connections changes, a proportional and much larger change occurs in the voltage between the output and the zero of the power supply. We can define the characteristics of the op-amp in terms of various parameters. In this book the important ones are:

(a) *Open-loop gain* – the ratio $\Delta V_{out}/\Delta V_{in}$, where ΔV_{out} and ΔV_{in} respresent the changes in V_{out} and V_{in}, respectively.
(b) *Input resistance* – the equivalent resistance which, if connected across the input in place of the op-amp circuit, would have the same effect on V_{in}.
(c) *Output resistance* – the internal resistance of the op-amp output. (The op-amp output behaves like a battery with internal resistance.)
(d) *Slew rate* – the maximum rate at which the output voltage can change when the input voltage is changed.

From these definitions, we can specify the *ideal op-amp*. It has infinite open-loop gain, so the presence of any input voltage drives the output to *saturation* (the maximum positive or negative voltage). It has infinite input resistance, so it does not load the input circuit. It has zero output resistance, so it may drive any load efficiently, and it responds instantaneously to input changes (infinite slew rate).

All the circuits in this book assume that real op-amps behave in an ideal way. All the calculations assume ideal behaviour, so that the overall performance of the circuit depends on components external to the op-amp rather than on the properties of the op-amp itself.

4.3 The 741 and other op-amps

It is possible to construct electronic op-amps using thermionic valves, discrete transistors or integrated circuits. These last are by far the most satisfactory, and this book will confine itself to them. Figure 4.1 shows the performance parameters for two integrated circuit op-amps alongside the same parameters for the ideal op-amp. The 741 is the most popular general purpose op-amp and the TL 081 is a modern replacement for the 741. The circuits in this book are designed for the 741 but will work with the TL 081.

Figure 4.1

parameter	ideal op-amp	741 op-amp	TL 081 op-amp
open-loop gain	infinite	10^5 *	10^5
input resistance	infinite	$2\,M\Omega$	$10^{12}\,\Omega$
output resistance	zero	$75\,\Omega$ †	$100\,\Omega$
slew rate	infinite	$10^6\,V\,s^{-1}$	$10^7\,V\,s^{-1}$

* The open-loop gain decreases as the frequency increases, becoming 1 at 1 MHz.
† The output is protected against short circuits. The maximum current is 25 mA.

Both op-amps come in plastic packages with 8 pins. They require balanced power supplies of $(-5\,V, 0, +5\,V)$ up to $(-15\,V, 0, +15\,V)$.* Suitable circuits for these are shown in appendix II. These op-amps will survive their outputs being short-circuited, and input voltages of up to $\pm 15\,V$. The pin connections for both op-amps are shown in figure 4.2.

Figure 4.3 gives the circuit diagram symbol for an op-amp. The plus $(+)$ and minus $(-)$ signs shown alongside the two inputs do not imply any polarity for the inputs. The $(-)$ input is called the *inverting input* because, when that input goes positive with respect to the other input, the output goes negative. The $(+)$ input is called the *non-inverting input* because, when that input goes positive with respect to the other input, the output also goes positive. Take care over the various voltage levels encountered in op-amp circuits. The op-amp amplifies the voltage between the inputs and not the voltage between an input and the power supply zero. For instance, an input voltage of 0.1 V can arise from one input being at $+3.0\,V$ relative to the zero and the other being at $+3.1\,V$ relative to the zero. All voltages are differences in potential between two points, and you may not assume that one of these points is always the power supply zero line. For the experiments in this book, the output voltage of the op-amp is measured relative to the power supply zero because measuring instruments like the oscilloscope will only measure voltages between their input terminals and zero or ground.

A further look at the pin-out diagram (figure 4.2) shows that pins 1 and 5 are labelled *offset null*. For the circuits used in this book these connections are not required, so they are omitted from circuit diagrams. Their use is described in appendix II. The connections to the power supply (V^- and V^+ to pins 4 and 7, respectively) are required for all circuits but are not shown on the circuit diagrams either.

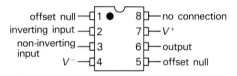

offset null — 1 ● 8 — no connection
inverting input — 2   7 — V^+
non-inverting input — 3   6 — output
V^- — 4   5 — offset null

Figure 4.2   Pin connections for the 741 and TL 081 op-amps

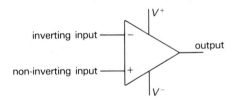

V^+
inverting input — $-$
               output
non-inverting input — $+$
V^-

Figure 4.3   The symbol for an op-amp

Hints for setting up op-amps

(a) Switch off the power supply when modifying a circuit and then check the circuit before reconnecting it.
(b) Remember that V^- and V^+ are negative and positive power supplies relative to zero, and neither of them should be grounded. (V^- is not zero or ground.)
(c) Do not confuse the $(+)$ and $(-)$ labels on the inputs with the power supply connections.
(d) Because only a tiny current flows into the inputs of the op-amp, there must always

* Whereas digital circuits operate between ground (logic 0) and a positive voltage (logic 1), analogue signals can be either positive or negative relative to ground. Therefore analogue circuits require power supplies that provide both positive and negative voltages relative to ground. When analogue signals are restricted to positive voltages, op-amp circuits of the form shown in section 8.2 may be used.

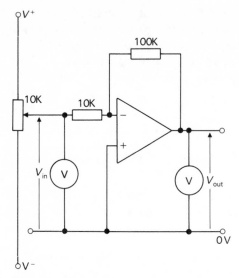

Figure 4.4   The inverting amplifier

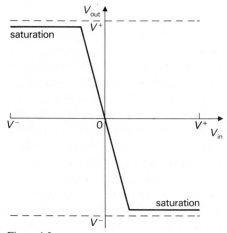

Figure 4.5

be a d.c. path to both inputs. (If charge can leak onto and collect at an input, the amplifier output will always be driven to saturation at either V^+ or V^-.)

(e) When possible, use an oscilloscope (CRO) or digital voltmeter (DVM) to measure voltages, because a moving-coil meter will often draw enough current to upset the correct operation of the circuit.

4.4   Op-amps and feedback

To produce a linear amplifier from an ideal op-amp, it is necessary to apply *feedback* to the op-amp. With feedback, a portion of the output signal is fed back into one of the inputs, so that the resultant output voltage arises from the combined effect of the applied input voltage and the feedback voltage. In *negative* feedback, part of the output signal is fed back to the inverting input. In *positive* feedback, the feedback signal is fed to the non-inverting input.

Here are two useful rules to predict the behaviour of a circuit containing an ideal op-amp with negative feedback.

Rule 1

The input current into the op-amp is zero.

This rule follows from the assumption of infinite input resistance.

Rule 2

When a voltage is applied between the inputs of an op-amp, the output potential changes in such a way as to enable the feedback components to return the two inputs to the same potential.

This rule is a consequence of the assumption of infinite gain for the ideal op-amp and the definition of negative feedback. Negative feedback helps the circuit to be stable.

Rules such as these do not explain how the op-amp works. They allow us, the users, to predict the behaviour of circuits. They must be applied to real circuits with care. Rule 1 will only apply when the currents flowing in the external components are much greater than any input current into the op-amp. Therefore any external resistor must have a resistance less than the input resistance of the op-amp. Rule 2 can only apply to that region in which V_{out} does change. When the amplifier reaches saturation (i.e. V_{out} approaches V^+ or V^-), further changes in the input voltage cannot change V_{out}, so rule 2 ceases to apply. Also, the finite slew rate of a real op-amp results in a time-lag between the input voltage changing and the output voltage changing in such a way as to negate the change in input voltage.

Questions

1 Does the output go more positive or more negative as the input goes more positive?
2 Deduce the change in V_{out} for a 1 V change in V_{in} when V_{in} is approximately (a) V^-, (b) 0 V and (c) V^+.
3 Over what range of values of V_{in} could the op-amp be said to amplify?

4.5   The op-amp with negative feedback – the inverting amplifier

Set up the circuit shown in figure 4.4. Remember that the power supply connections are not shown on the circuit diagram. Connect two voltmeters to measure the input voltage V_{in} and the output voltage V_{out}. Record the value of V_{out} as you vary V_{in} from V^- to V^+. Plot your results on a graph of V_{out} against V_{in}. Such a graph is called the *transfer characteristic* of the circuit, and its form is shown in figure 4.5.

Use the transfer characteristic graph to answer the questions.

The circuit in figure 4.4. uses the op-amp in its *inverting mode*. When a positive voltage V_{in} is applied to resistor R_{in} (see figure 4.6), the inverting input will go positive

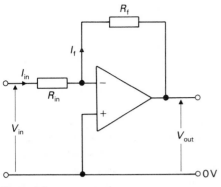

Figure 4.6

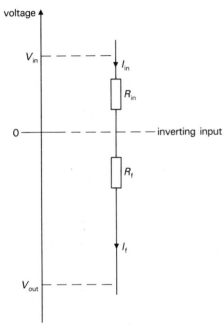

Figure 4.7

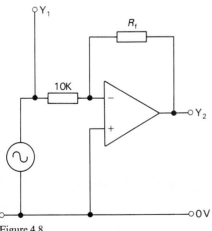

Figure 4.8

and the output V_{out} will go negative. Rule 1 states that no current flows into the input of the op-amp, so the current I_{in} flowing through R_{in} must equal the current I_f flowing through the feedback resistor R_f which connects the output to the input. The gain of the op-amp is so high that the two inputs must be at nearly the same potential. The non-inverting input is earthed, so the inverting input must also be within a few millivolts of zero or earth potential. In this configuration we call the inverting input a *virtual earth*. R_{in} and R_f form a potential divider between V_{in} (positive) and V_{out} (negative), with the junction between them at effectively earth potential (see figure 4.7).

Using Ohm's law $V_{out} = -I_f R_f$

and $V_{in} = I_{in} R_{in}$

Therefore $\dfrac{V_{out}}{V_{in}} = \dfrac{-I_f R_f}{I_{in} R_{in}}$

$$= \frac{-R_f}{R_{in}} \quad \text{since } I_{in} = I_f$$

The ratio V_{out}/V_{in} is the *closed-loop gain* (with negative feedback applied), and in this circuit it is the ratio of the feedback resistance to the input resistance. This illustrates rule 2 – when the input signal makes the inverting input go positive, the output will go sufficiently negative for the current through the feedback resistor to return the inverting input to zero, which is the same potential as the non-inverting input.

4.6 Further experiments with the inverting amplifier

Set up the circuit shown in figure 4.8. The symbol $\ominus$ represents a sine-wave signal generator and Y_1 and Y_2 are two points at which to monitor the time variation of the potential with respect to zero. If you have a double-beam oscilloscope, these points are connected to the Y_1 and Y_2-inputs. With a single-beam oscilloscope, connect the Y-input to Y_1 to monitor the input signal, and to Y_2 to monitor the output signal.

Carry out the experiments suggested below. Remember, when you are making these measurements, that you are trying to get a wide-ranging picture of the behaviour of an op-amp. Individual measurements will have uncertainties, owing to the departure of the op-amp from ideal behaviour, the tolerance in resistor values and calibration errors in the measuring instruments. So when you change a resistor value, change it by a factor of three or ten rather than by 10 per cent. Similarly, when you change the frequency, change it by factors of three or ten.

(a) Show that when $R_f = 10\,k\Omega$, the gain of the op-amp is unity and the output is the inverse of the input.

(b) Measure the closed-loop gain for various values of R_f (e.g. $100\,k\Omega$ and $1\,M\Omega$).

(c) Investigate how the closed-loop gain varies with the frequency of a small-amplitude input signal, for a fixed value of the feedback resistor R_f.

Do your results agree with the rules concerning the behaviour of the ideal op-amp?

Questions

4 What value would R_f have if the circuit in figure 4.8 had a closed-loop gain of 20?

5 What would be the predicted value of the closed-loop gain of the circuit in figure 4.8 if R_f was $50\,M\Omega$? Why would you not expect this prediction to be correct for the 741?

6 Sketch the time variation of V_{out} when V_{in} varies sinusoidally with an amplitude of V^+ and a frequency of 50 Hz. Refer to figure 4.5 to help you work this out for $R_f = 100\,k\Omega$.

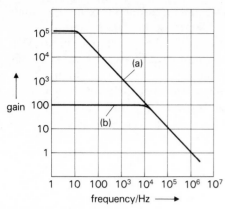

Figure 4.9   The frequency response of the 741 op-amp

They should be a good approximation, leading you to the following conclusions about the inverting amplifier with negative feedback:

(a) The closed-loop gain of the amplifier with negative feedback depends only on the values of the external resistors so long as it is very much smaller than the open-loop gain of the op-amp. This result is of great value in circuit design, since it makes the overall gain of the amplifier independent of variations due to manufacturing tolerances in the op-amp.

(b) The gain of the amplifier decreases as the frequency of the input signal increases. The use of negative feedback increases the range of frequencies over which the gain is constant: the 741 with feedback that gives a closed-loop gain of 100 can cope with audio frequencies up to 10 kHz. Figure 4.9 shows the frequency response for a 741 op-amp, with the graph for the open-loop gain labelled (a) and that for a closed-loop gain of 100 labelled (b).

The range of frequencies over which the gain of the amplifier is approximately constant is called the *band width*. The band width of an op-amp extends from zero to that frequency at which the closed-loop gain has dropped to $1/\sqrt{2}$ of its value for an ideal op-amp.

4.7   The non-inverting amplifier

Figure 4.10 shows a circuit for a *non-inverting amplifier*. Set up the circuit with the input voltage derived from a potentiometer connected between V^- and V^+. Choose a value of 100 kΩ for R_f and plot out the transfer characteristic of the amplifier. Show that it behaves as a non-inverting amplifier; that is, when V_{in} goes more positive, V_{out} also goes more positive (see figure 4.11).

Replace the potentiometer with a signal generator and use an oscilloscope to measure and monitor the input and output voltages V_{in} and V_{out}. Measure the closed-loop gain of the amplifier with this configuration for several values of the feedback resistor R_f (suitable values for R_f are 10 kΩ, 100 kΩ and 1 MΩ). Investigate whether the frequency response is the same for the non-inverting and the inverting amplifiers.

We can explain the behaviour of the circuit in terms of our rules as follows. Rule 1 states that no current flows into either input. Therefore (a) the input resistance to the zero of the power supply at the non-inverting input is equal to R_1 and (b) the current I_f flowing in R_f is the same as the current flowing in R_2. When a voltage V_{in} is applied to the non-inverting input, rule 2 tells us that the output voltage V_{out} will change to bring the two inputs to the same potential. This happens when a current I_f flows through R_f and R_2 of such a magnitude that

$$V_{in} = I_f R_2$$

However $$V_{out} = I_f (R_f + R_2)$$

Eliminating I_f $$\frac{V_{out}}{V_{in}} = \frac{(R_f + R_2)}{R_2}$$

In the operating region of our ideal op-amp, a change ΔV_{in} in V_{in} will produce a change ΔV_{out} in V_{out} such that the closed-loop gain is

$$\frac{\Delta V_{out}}{\Delta V_{in}} = \frac{(R_f + R_2)}{R_2}$$

Check that this agrees with your measurements.

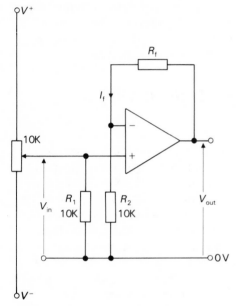

Figure 4.10   The non-inverting amplifier

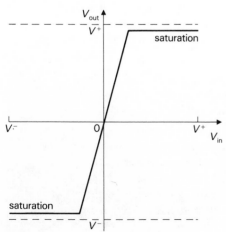

Figure 4.11

Questions

7 Show that the input resistance of the circuit in figure 4.10 is 10 kΩ.

8 Calculate the range of input voltages over which the amplifier will behave linearly when R_f in figure 4.10 is 100 kΩ.

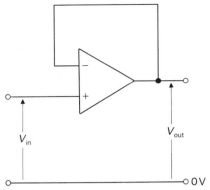

Figure 4.12   The buffer, or voltage follower

4.8 The buffer or voltage follower

Figure 4.12 shows a very simple circuit called a *buffer*. The output is directly connected to the inverting input, giving 100 per cent negative feedback. We will use this circuit for isolating signals and for matching a high-resistance source as input into a low-resistance load.

> **Question**
>
> **9** Predict the gain and input resistance of the buffer circuit in figure 4.12.

4.9 The differential amplifier or comparator

The operational amplifier circuits studied in sections 4.5 and 4.6 used the op-amp to amplify voltages between the input signal point and ground or zero. However, changes in the output potential V_{out} occur when a voltage appears between the two inputs, so we may use the op-amp to detect and amplify the difference between two signals.

Figure 4.13 shows a suitable circuit. Set it up with all four resistors R_{in} and R_f having the value of 10 kΩ. Use voltmeters to measure V_{in} and V_{out}. (Since V_{in} is not measured with respect to earth or zero, you cannot use an oscilloscope to measure V_{in} because it will only measure voltages between the Y-input and earth.) Adjust the two 10 kΩ potentiometers R_1 and R_2 to vary V_1 and V_2, and show that V_{out} is proportional to $-V_{in} = -(V_1 - V_2)$, and not to V_1 or V_2 alone.

With these resistance values, V_{out} should equal $-V_{in}$ in this circuit because we are using an inverting amplifier. For this circuit, R_{in} and R_f have the same values for both inputs, though R_{in} need not be equal to R_f. Since no current flows into either input, the current in each resistor R_{in} is the same as that in its associated R_f (rule 1). The pairs of resistors R_{in} and R_f act as potential dividers – between V_2 and zero for the non-inverting input, between V_1 and V_{out} for the inverting input (see figure 4.14). By rule 2, V_{out} will change until both inputs of the op-amp are at the same potential, V. For the non-inverting input, V is given by

$$V = V_2\left(\frac{R_f}{R_f + R_{in}}\right)$$

For the inverting input, V is given by

$$V = (V_1 - V_{out})\left(\frac{R_f}{R_f + R_{in}}\right) + V_{out}$$

Eliminating V, and remembering that $V_{in} = (V_1 - V_2)$, gives

$$\frac{V_{out}}{V_{in}} = \frac{-R_f}{R_{in}}$$

Again we find that the closed-loop gain depends only on the values of external components and not on the properties of the op-amp so long as these properties approximate to those of the ideal op-amp.

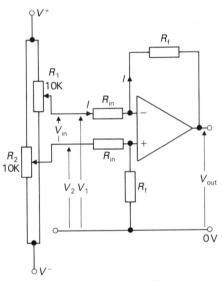

Figure 4.13   The differential amplifier

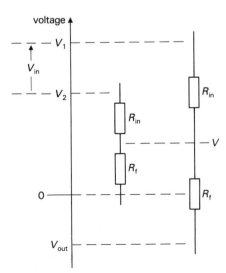

Figure 4.14

> **Question**
>
> **10** In section 4.9, it was suggested you made all four external resistors in figure 4.13 the same value, 10 kΩ. Predict the relationship between V_{in} and V_{out} when both R_{in} resistors are of value 10 kΩ and both R_f resistors have a resistance of 100 kΩ.

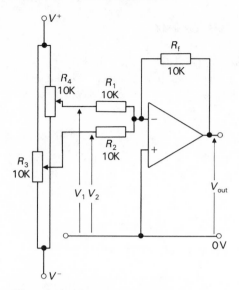

Figure 4.15   The summing amplifier

4.10   The summing amplifier

The summing amplifier uses an op-amp to add two or more voltages and produces an output that is proportional to their sum.

Figure 4.15 shows the circuit for a simple summing amplifier with two inputs. Investigate the behaviour of this circuit with $R_1 = R_2 = R_f = 10\,k\Omega$, and show that V_{out} equals $-(V_1 + V_2)$.

Rule 1 states that no current flows into the inverting input. Thus the current in R_f equals the sum of the currents in R_1 and R_2. The non-inverting input is at zero potential, and rule 2 tells us that the inverting input must also be effectively at zero potential. Therefore

$$\text{Current in } R_1 + \text{Current in } R_2 = \text{Current in } R_f$$

$$\frac{V_1}{R_1} + \frac{V_2}{R_2} = \frac{-V_{out}}{R_f}$$

For the case where $R_1 = R_2 = R_f$,

$$V_{out} = -(V_1 + V_2)$$

Both the sum and difference amplifiers have been studied with steady voltages applied to the inputs. Replace the potentiometers (R_1 and R_2 in figure 4.13, and R_3 and R_4 in figure 4.15) with inputs such as a signal generator and a low-voltage transformer.

4.11   Positive feedback and the Schmitt trigger

In the circuits studied so far, the feedback from the output has been to the inverting input. It has been negative feedback, and rule 2 has enabled you to predict the behaviour of these circuits. When feedback is applied to the non-inverting input, the output moves quickly to the limit of the power supply. This is *positive* feedback. Our first circuit that incorporates positive feedback is the Schmitt trigger circuit.

With zero input the Schmitt trigger circuit is stable, with the output at approximately V^+ or V^-. When the output is at V^-, a positive input signal that is greater than some predetermined value changes the output very rapidly from V^- to V^+. Positive feedback speeds up the change, and holds the output at V^+ even if the input signal is removed. When a sufficient negative input signal arrives, the output switches back from V^+ to V^-, with positive feedback holding the output at V^- when the signal is removed.

Figure 4.16 shows a simple Schmitt trigger circuit for investigation. Vary the potential at point A by using the potentiometer R, and observe the sudden change in V_{out} from approximately V^- to approximately V^+ as V_{in} goes positive from zero. Vary

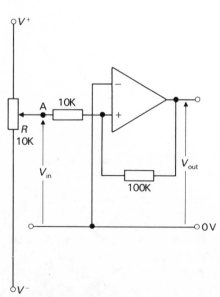

Figure 4.16   The Schmitt trigger

Figure 4.17

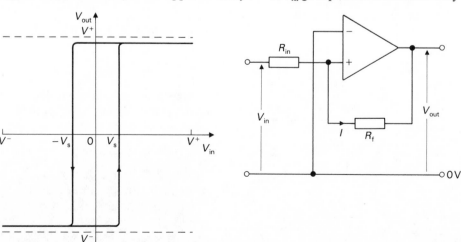

Figure 4.18

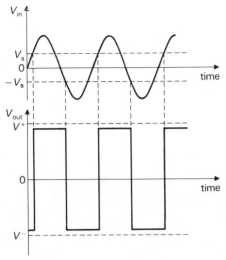

Figure 4.19

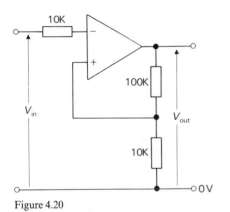

Figure 4.20

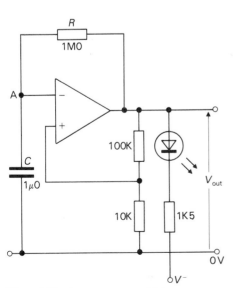

Figure 4.21   A square-wave oscillator

V_{in} cyclically from V^- to V^+ and back again, and plot a graph of V_{out} against V_{in} (figure 4.17). The range of voltages V_{in} between the two switch-over points is known as the *hysteresis* of the circuit. Use different values for the two resistors and find out how they affect the hysteresis of the circuit.

Think about the circuit shown in figure 4.18 at a time when V_{in} is zero and V_{out} is approximately V^-. The inverting input is at zero, and by rule 1 no current flows into the non-inverting input. The current I flowing through R_f and R_{in} keeps the non-inverting input at $V^- R_{in}/(R_f + R_{in})$ and hence drives V_{out} to saturation near V^-. As V_{in} goes positive, the potential of the non-inverting input rises until, when V_{in}/R_{in} is $-V^-/R_f$, the potential of both inputs is zero. Any further rise in V_{in} results in the output switching from V^- to nearly V^+, being driven and held by the positive feedback through R_f. When V_{in} drops to $-(R_{in}/R_f)V^+$, the non-inverting input again changes sign and switches from V^+ to V^-.

Replace the potentiometer R in figure 4.16 with a signal generator. Observe how the output waveform changes when you vary the shape, amplitude and frequency of the input wave.

Figure 4.19 displays the output waveform of a Schmitt trigger circuit for which the input is a sine wave. The switching voltage V_s is given by

$$V_s = \left(\frac{R_{in}}{R_f}\right) V_{out}$$

The Schmitt trigger circuit is so useful for providing sharp square-edged pulses from a variety of input waveforms that it is manufactured as a specific integrated circuit. The TTL 7414 and CMOS 40106, for instance, both contain six inverting Schmitt triggers on a single chip.

Questions

13 Predict the variation of V_{out} with time when $R_f = R_{in}$ and V_{in} is a sine wave of amplitude V^+.
14 Describe how V_{out} varies with time if the amplitude of V_{in} is less than V_s.
15 Write out an explanation of the working of the inverting Schmitt trigger circuit shown in figure 4.20.

4.12   A square-wave oscillator

With a combination of positive feedback and a timing circuit we can use the op-amp as an oscillator. Figure 4.21 shows a form of oscillator called a *relaxation oscillator*, in which the timing action arises from charging and discharging the capacitor C through the resistor R.

The circuit shown in figure 4.21 also has an LED indicator to indicate when the output is approximately V^+. Set up the circuit and measure the period of the oscillations for various values of R and C. Use an oscilloscope to monitor the waveforms at the output and at point A (the inverting input) of the op-amp.

Positive feedback from the 100 kΩ and 10 kΩ resistors to the non-inverting input ensures that the output is always near either V^+ or V^-. Whether it is V^+ or V^- depends on whether the non-inverting input is positive or negative with respect to the inverting input. The potential of the inverting input is determined by the p.d. across the capacitor C which charges or discharges through the resistor R.

So imagine that when the circuit is initially switched on, the capacitor C is uncharged and the output is high ($V_{out} = V^+$). The non-inverting input is held at $\sim 0.1\, V^+$ by the 100 kΩ and 10 kΩ resistors, which ensures that the output remains at V^+. Capacitor C now charges up through resistor R until the voltage across it is $\sim 0.1\, V^+$: the two inputs of the op-amp are then at the same potential. As the capacitor charges further, the inverting input becomes positive relative to the non-

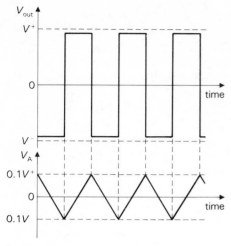

Figure 4.22

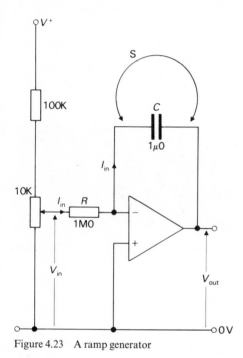

Figure 4.23   A ramp generator

inverting input, so the output V_{out} switches from V^+ to V^-. The capacitor C now discharges through R and then charges up with the opposite polarity until the voltage across it is $\sim 0.1\ V^-$. At this moment, the two inputs are once again at the same potential. As the inverting input goes more negative than the non-inverting input, V_{out} switches from V^- to V^+, and so on.

Figure 4.22 shows typical waveforms for the output and the inverting input (point A). The output spends equal times near V^+ and near V^-. The output wave is said to have a *mark-to-space ratio* of 1.

Questions

16 The period of oscillation is proportional to RC. Give values for R and C that would make the period one-fifth of its value in figure 4.21.
17 Explain the effect of changing the ratio of the two resistors that provide the positive feedback.
18 Devise a circuit to produce a variable-frequency oscillator.
19 Should the period of the oscillations depend on the voltage of the power supply?

Other types of relaxation oscillator can be made from logic gates (see chapter 3). A specially designed relaxation oscillator using two op-amps and a bistable is the 555 timer, which is discussed in chapter 8.

4.13   A ramp generator

All the circuits so far have used resistors for the feedback components. Figure 4.23 shows an op-amp with negative feedback through a capacitor C.

Set up the circuit with the values of R and C shown in the figure. The flying lead S is used to discharge the capacitor. Adjust the potentiometer to give an input voltage V_{in} of 0.1 V and record the value of V_{out} as a function of time (take readings every 10 s), starting with time zero when the capacitor is discharged. Take sets of readings of V_{out} against time for different values of V_{in} and deduce a relation between V_{out} and V_{in}.

With R equal to 1 MΩ and C equal to 1 µF, the *time constant* of the circuit (RC) equals 1 s. Investigate the effect on the relation between V_{out} and time, of using different values of R and C while keeping V_{in} constant at 0.1 V.

Figures 4.24 and 4.25 show the forms of the graphs from these two sets of readings. Until V_{out} saturates it is proportional to V_{in} multiplied by time. Can you explain the operation of the circuit in figure 4.23?

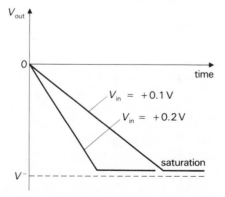

Figure 4.24   The effect of changing V_{in}

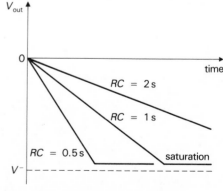

Figure 4.25   The effect of changing RC

Initially the capacitor C is uncharged and V_{in} is connected to a constant positive potential with respect to zero. The voltage V_{in} that is applied to the inverting input drives a current I_{in} through resistance R. No current flows into the inverting input

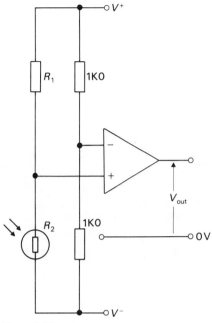

Figure 4.26

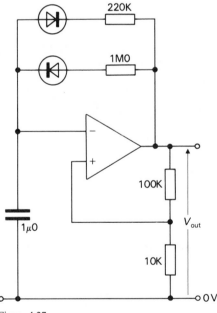

Figure 4.27

(rule 1) so this current flows to charge the capacitor C. The non-inverting input is at zero potential, and rule 2 states that V_{out} will change so as to keep both inputs at the same potential. Therefore the inverting input will stay at zero potential. The voltage across a capacitor is proportional to the charge stored. A constant value of V_{in} implies a constant current I_{in} to charge the capacitor. This constant rate of flow of charge onto the capacitor will result in the voltage across the capacitor changing at a constant rate. Thus V_{out} will change at a constant rate and the graph of V_{out} against time will be a straight line.

This argument may be given mathematical form using calculus. For this inverting amplifier

$$V_{in} = I_{in}R \quad \text{and} \quad V_{out} = \frac{-Q}{C} \quad \text{since the inverting input is a virtual earth.}$$

The charge Q on the capacitor $= \int I_{in}\,dt$

Substituting for Q gives $\quad V_{out} = \int \left(\frac{-1}{C}\right) I_{in}\,dt$

$$= \frac{-1}{RC} \int V_{in}\,dt$$

where RC is called the time constant of the circuit. From this analysis the circuit is called an *integrating circuit*.

The integrator forms the basis of frequency and rate meters, and is of major importance for the analogue computer.

The ramp generator completes this first look at circuits using operational amplifiers. Further circuits using op-amps are described in chapter 8.

4.14 Further questions

1 Draw circuit diagrams for (a) inverting and (b) non-inverting amplifiers with closed-loop gains of 30.
2 In figure 4.26, R_2 is a light-dependent resistor whose resistance decreases when light falls on it. In the dark, $R_2 > R_1$, and when it is illuminated, $R_2 < R_1$. Deduce how V_{out} changes when R_2 is covered up or illuminated, and suggest a use for the circuit.
3 Draw a circuit for a non-inverting Schmitt trigger which will produce square-edged output pulses for any input pulses of amplitude greater than $0.2V^+$.
4 Draw a circuit using a single op-amp for a summing amplifier that will give an output $V_{out} = 5(V_1 + 2V_2)$, where V_1 and V_2 are the two input voltages.
5 A low-resistance microphone generates a waveform of peak amplitude $20\,mV$ when recording. Draw a circuit diagram of an amplifier suitable for producing an output of $1.0\,V$ peak amplitude.
6 Draw the output waveform you would expect from the circuit in figure 4.27. How will it differ from that obtained from the circuit in figure 4.21? What is the mark-to-space ratio for the output waveform?

5 Diodes and transistors

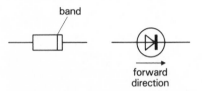

Figure 5.1   Conventional symbol for a diode

5.1   The silicon *pn* junction diode

Many electrical circuits require a device that will conduct in one direction and not in the other. The silicon *pn* junction diode is one such device. Ideally, it should have zero resistance to current flowing in the *forward* direction and infinite resistance to current flowing in the *reverse* direction. A silicon diode suitable for the experiments in this chapter is the 1N4001. Its specification is given in figure 5.2.

Maximum average forward current	I_f	1 A
Forward voltage drop at $I_f = 1$ A	V_f	1 V
Maximum repetitive reverse voltage	V_{rrm}	50 V
Reverse current at V_{rrm}	I_r	50 μA

Figure 5.2   Data for 1N4001

When working under the two sets of conditions shown in figure 5.2, it has a forward resistance of 1 Ω and a reverse resistance of 1 MΩ respectively, so it approximates quite well to the ideal. To investigate its characteristics more closely, set up the circuit in figure 5.3. Measure the forward voltage drop across the diode with an oscilloscope, and the current through the diode, as you vary the supply voltage from 0 to 5 V. Plot your results to obtain the *forward bias* part of the characteristic. Then reverse the diode and repeat the process, to obtain the *reverse bias* part of the characteristic. The full characteristic has the form shown in figure 5.4.

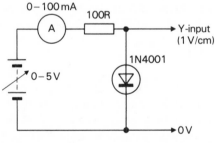

Figure 5.3

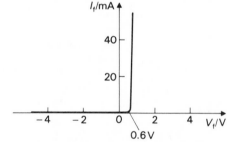

Figure 5.4   Typical characteristic of 1N4001

The important points to notice from the graph are that the diode does not start to conduct until the forward voltage drop is about 0.6 V and that the forward voltage drop does not rise much above 0.6 V. This 0.6 V has important consequences in the design of some circuits with silicon *pn* junctions, particularly when using bipolar junction transistors. (This will be discussed later in this chapter.) Notice also that the forward resistance decreases as the current increases.

5.2   Using an oscilloscope to display diode characteristics

It is useful and saves time to be able to display the characteristics of devices on an oscilloscope screen instead of plotting them on paper. The diode characteristic is a

Questions

1 The variable voltage in figure 5.3 is to be obtained from a fixed-voltage supply of 5 V and a 1 kΩ potentiometer. The maximum current required is 50 mA. Draw the circuit for this and calculate the minimum power rating of the potentiometer.

2 Calculate the minimum power rating for the 100 Ω resistor in figure 5.3. What would be the result of omitting this resistor?

3 Use the graph in figure 5.4 to calculate the forward resistance of a 1N4001 at currents of 10 mA and 40 mA.

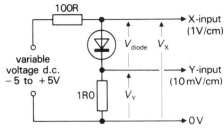

Figure 5.5

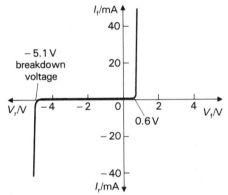

Figure 5.6   Characteristic of a 5.1 V Zener diode

Questions

4 A voltage is applied to the circuit in figure 5.5 such that there is an X-deflection of 0.7 cm and a Y-deflection of 2.0 cm. Calculate
(a) V_X and V_Y;
(b) V_Y as a percentage of V_X;
(c) the current through the diode.
5 What would be the effect on the characteristic displayed by the circuit in figure 5.5 of swapping the Y-input and common connections to the oscilloscope? Would there be any advantage in doing this?
6 The BZY88 series of Zener diodes can dissipate a maximum of 500 mW. Calculate the maximum reverse current that can safely be passed through a BZY88, 5.1 V Zener diode.

current–voltage plot, but the majority of oscilloscopes are only provided with high-resistance voltage inputs. A current can be displayed on an oscilloscope by passing it through a low-value resistor and then measuring the voltage across the resistor, since the voltage across a resistor is proportional to the current through it.

Switch off the oscilloscope time base, adjust the X and Y-sensitivities to those indicated in figure 5.5, and centre the spot. If it is not possible to adjust the X-sensitivity, then find out what it is in volts per division.

Set up the circuit in figure 5.5. If radio frequency pick-up on the Y-input is making a short vertical line, put a 0.1 μF capacitor between the Y-input and the 0 V terminal of the oscilloscope to remove it. Vary the supply voltage slowly from −5 V to +5 V and observe the diode characteristic being 'drawn' on the oscilloscope screen.

Next substitute a 3 V, 50 Hz a.c. voltage supply for the variable-voltage d.c. supply. This will give a continuous display of the characteristic.

There is one problem which frequently occurs when using oscilloscopes. Voltage measurements, V_X and V_Y, are made relative to a common terminal, which is earthed. This can hamper measurements in a number of ways. In this case, the voltage V_Y across the 1 Ω resistor is included in the V_X measurement, which is supposed to be the voltage across the diode only, V_{diode}. This is why the resistor has a low value of 1 Ω, so that the voltage across it is small compared with V_X. Consequently the displayed curve is close to the true characteristic.

Use the circuit in figure 5.5 to display the characteristics of the following diodes, which are all used in this book.

Germanium point-contact diode (OA91)

The point to notice about the germanium diode is that it starts to conduct between 0.1 and 0.2 V, making it suitable for low-voltage applications such as the demodulation of radio signals (see section 6.7). However, silicon is preferred for most applications because silicon diodes can handle higher currents at higher temperatures and have higher reverse breakdown voltages ($V_{r.r.m.}$).

Light-emitting diode (RS red standard 0.2-inch LED)

The a.c. supply should not exceed 3 V (r.m.s.) so that the maximum reverse voltage of the diode is not exceeded. This diode starts to conduct when the forward voltage is about 2 V.

Zener diode (BZY88, 5.1 V)

In order to display the characteristic of this Zener diode a slightly higher voltage is required: set the a.c. supply to 5 V (r.m.s.).

All semi-conductor diodes have a reverse breakdown voltage. The important difference with the Zener diode is that the breakdown voltage has been lowered to a few volts. The very steep gradient of the characteristic at the breakdown voltage ensures that the reverse voltage across the diode remains almost constant over a wide range of reverse currents (see figure 5.6). For this reason, Zener diodes are widely used to provide reference voltages in power supplies.

5.3   Rectification of a.c.

For most power supplies a transformer is used to step down the a.c. mains to the required voltage. Then the a.c. is rectified to d.c. using diodes, and smoothed using capacitors.

Set up the circuit in figure 5.7 with the time base set at 1 ms/cm, and display the waveform of V_{in} on an oscilloscope. Next display the waveform of V_{out}, which gives a half-wave rectified sine wave. Notice that the peak value of V_{out} is about 0.6 V less than the peak value of V_{in}, owing to the voltage drop across the diode (see figure 5.8).

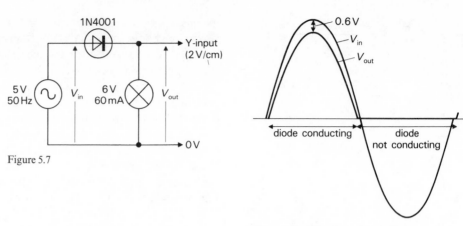

Figure 5.7

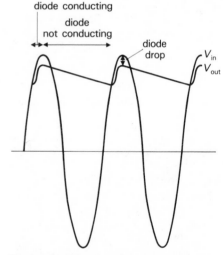

Figure 5.8   Waveforms in a half-wave rectification circuit

Most electronic equipment requires d.c. that is smooth and unfluctuating, unlike that produced by the diode alone. A simple smoothing circuit is made by adding a capacitor, called a *reservoir capacitor*, to the circuit in figure 5.7, as shown in figure 5.9. Before adding the reservoir capacitor to your circuit, you should ask yourself what effect it will have on

(a) the brightness of the bulb;
(b) the waveform of the voltage across the bulb, V_{out};
(c) the fraction of the cycle during which the diode conducts.

Then alter the time base setting to 5 ms/cm and check to see if your predictions are correct (see figure 5.10).

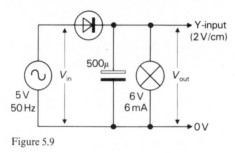

Figure 5.9

Figure 5.10   Waveforms in a half-wave rectification circuit with reservoir capacitor

Questions

The questions below refer to figure 5.9.

7 Calculate the time constant for the discharge of the capacitor through the bulb. How does this compare with the period of the a.c. supply?

8 What would be the effect on the waveform of V_{out} of disconnecting the bulb? Try it.

9 What would be the effect of reducing the reservoir capacitor to 50 µF on (a) the time constant, (b) the waveform of V_{out} and (c) the bulb brightness? Try it. Explain why the brightness of the bulb changes.

5.4   The bipolar silicon junction transistor

Bipolar junction transistors (usually called simply *transistors*) are amongst the most widely used devices in electronics today, either in the form of discrete components or in integrated circuits. They perform two important functions: *amplification* and *switching*. The transistor suggested for the experiments in this book is the 2N3053 (see

Figure 5.11   Conventional symbol for an *npn* transistor and underside view of 2N3053

Maximum collector current	$I_{c,max}$	1 A
Maximum power dissipation	P_{max}	800 mW
Typical current gain	h_{FE}	150

Figure 5.12   Data for 2N3053

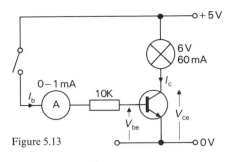

Figure 5.13

figure 5.12) because it is sufficiently robust to be used in all the experiments, but there are other silicon transistors which could be used.

The voltage of the power supply for the circuits described in this chapter is not critical. 5 V is suggested, but 6 V from a battery would work equally well.

5.5 The transistor as a current-operated switch

Set up the circuit in figure 5.13 so that by operating the switch you are able to turn the light on and off. The normal current for the bulb is about 60 mA, yet it is being turned on by a current of about 0.5 mA into the base of the transistor, i.e. the transistor is behaving as a current-operated switch.

Now consider the collector–emitter voltage, V_{ce}. When the transistor is switched off it should have infinite resistance, so V_{ce} should be equal to the supply voltage, but when the transistor is switched on it should have zero resistance, so V_{ce} should be zero. Check this using an oscilloscope as a voltmeter.

Next measure the base–emitter voltage, V_{be}. When the transistor is switched on V_{be} rises from 0 to 0.6 V. The base–emitter junction behaves like a diode: it does not conduct until the voltage across it is 0.6 V, but after that the voltage across it rises very little. The purpose of the 10 kΩ resistor in series with the base is to limit the base current, because excessive base current would destroy the transistor.

When the transistor is used as a switch, the power dissipated is small: it is the collector current that is the limiting factor.

> **Question**
>
> **10** When a transistor is switched on, it has a collector–emitter voltage $V_{ce} = 0.2$ V and a collector current $I_c = 1$ A. Calculate the power dissipated when it is switched off, and when it is switched on.

5.6 A light-operated switch

The ORP12 light-dependent resistor has a resistance which varies depending on the light intensity falling on it (see figure 5.14).

light source	approximate resistance
bright sunlight	10 Ω
fluorescent tube	500 Ω
total darkness	10 MΩ

Figure 5.14 Data for ORP12

Except in very bright conditions, the current through it is insufficient to light a bulb from a low-voltage source, but is sufficient to switch on a transistor. To demonstrate this, set up the circuit in figure 5.15 and alternately cover and expose the light-dependent resistor. Notice that, like with a switch, the bulb turns on and off, but that, unlike with a switch, there are intermediate states where the bulb lights dimly. Not only can the collector current be turned on and off, it can be varied continuously as well. The remainder of this chapter deals with this continuous variation.

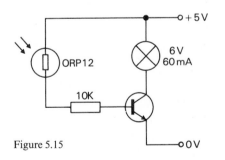

Figure 5.15

5.7 Characteristics of the transistor

The two important characteristics for the circuits in this book are the input characteristic (I_b–V_{be}) and the transfer characteristic (I_c–I_b).

(a) The input characteristic demonstrates that the base–emitter junction behaves like a *pn* junction diode. Set up the circuit in figure 5.16 and obtain readings of base current I_b, and base–emitter voltage V_{be}, in order to plot a graph similar to figure 5.17.

(b) The transfer characteristic demonstrates the *current amplification*. Use the circuit in figure 5.16 to obtain readings of the base current I_b, and the collector current I_c, in order to plot a graph similar to figure 5.18. Notice that the graph is almost

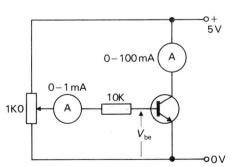

Figure 5.16

Question

11 Calculate the power dissipated in the transistor in figure 5.16 when the collector current is 160 mA. How do the current and power compare with the maximum ratings?

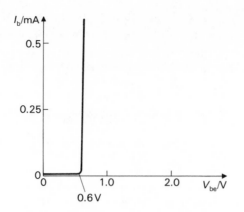

Figure 5.17 Typical input characteristic for a transistor

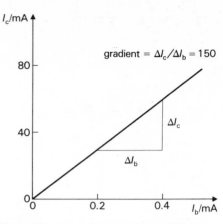

Figure 5.18 Typical transfer characteristic for a transistor

linear, the collector current being a constant factor (typically 150) greater than the base current, hence the term current amplification. The small base current controls the collector current through the transistor in much the same way as a tap controls the flow of water through it.

The d.c. current gain, h_{FE}, is defined as the ratio I_c/I_b. For the 2N3053 this varies from transistor to transistor over a range of values from 50 to 250, but is typically about 150.

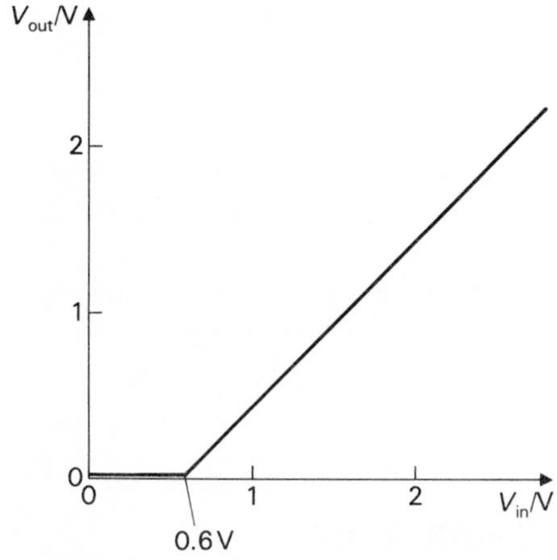

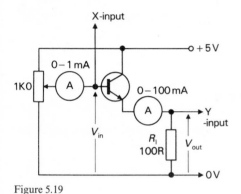

Figure 5.19

Figure 5.20

Figure 5.21

5.8 The emitter follower circuit

The integrated circuits used in the preceding chapters have superseded transistors in a vast number of applications, but transistors are still used where large currents are required. The circuit in figure 5.15 was used in conjunction with a light-dependent resistor to *switch* a bulb on or off. It could equally well have been used with the output of TTL or CMOS logic to *switch* a high-current relay. The emitter follower circuit is used in *linear* circuits where *current amplification* is required. For example, a 741 op-amp produces too small a current to operate a loudspeaker satisfactorily, but can be made to do so with an emitter follower circuit.

To demonstrate emitter follower action, set up the circuit in figure 5.19 and 'draw' the transfer characteristic on the screen (figure 5.20). Observe the following points:

(a) Provided the transistor is conducting, the emitter voltage V_{out} is 0.6 V less than the base voltage V_{in}.
(b) The current gain, I_{out}/I_{in}, remains nearly constant, and is equal to $h_{FE}+1$.
(c) The input resistance, V_{in}/I_{in}, is approximately $h_{FE}R_l$. The emitter follower has a high input resistance and a low output resistance.

To understand the operation of the circuit, assume that initially the input voltage is zero and the transistor is switched off. Now assume that the input voltage is rising. When it exceeds 0.6 V the transistor starts to conduct, causing a current through the load resistor R_l and a voltage across it. But the voltage across the load resistor reduces the base–emitter voltage, and so tends to stop the transistor conduction. As a result of this *negative feedback* action, the base–emitter voltage remains close to 0.6 V, independent of the input voltage, the load current and the load resistance. So the emitter voltage follows about 0.6 V behind the input voltage, hence the name emitter follower.

5.9 Circuits for variable-voltage power supplies

There are many occasions when a variable-voltage power supply is required. The simplest form is a potentiometer, but this has its limitations. Set up the circuit in figure 5.21 and adjust V_{out} to 3 V (measure it with an oscilloscope). Now connect a

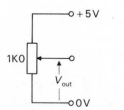

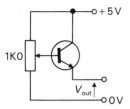

Figure 5.22   Emitter follower circuit

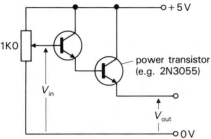

Figure 5.23   Darlington pair

Questions

13 If the supply voltage is 10.1 V in figure 5.24, calculate
(a) the current through the diode with no load on the output;
(b) the current through the diode when a load resistor of 1 kΩ is connected to the output;
(c) the resistance of the load resistor that will cause the diode to cease to conduct.

14 In the circuit in figure 5.26, the voltage of the supply is slowly increased from 0 to 12 V.
(a) Explain how the lamp and the Zener diode behave.
(b) Do any of the components exceed their maximum ratings?
The Zener diode is now reversed.
(c) Explain how the lamp and the Zener diode behave this time.
(d) Do any of the components exceed their maximum ratings this time?

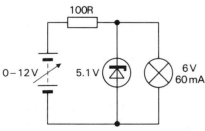

Figure 5.26

1 kΩ resistor as a load across the output and notice how the output voltage falls, owing to the output resistance of the potentiometer. The lower the load resistance, the more pronounced is this effect.

Next set up the circuit in figure 5.22, adjust V_{out} to 3 V and then connect a 1 kΩ load across it as before. This time the output voltage hardly drops at all. Substitute a 100 Ω resistor as a load and notice that the voltage still falls very little, demonstrating the low output resistance of the emitter follower. The output resistance can be lowered further by using two transistors in tandem, known as a *Darlington pair*, as in figure 5.23. In this case the output voltage is approximately 1.2 V (two 'diode drops') less than the input voltage.

Question

12 Potentiometers are frequently damaged by careless use. A typical 1 kΩ potentiometer can dissipate a maximum of 0.25 W. Calculate the minimum resistance that can be connected as a load to the potentiometer in figure 5.21 so that the potentiometer can safely be used over its entire range.

5.10   Stabilised power supply using a Zener diode

A frequent requirement of a power supply is a fixed voltage that is not affected by changes in the load current; for example, a fixed 5 V supply is required for TTL ICs. A Zener diode can be used to achieve this. Set up the circuit in figure 5.24. The Zener diode is reverse biased to its breakdown voltage of 5.1 V and conducts with a current of between 50 and 100 mA. Confirm that the output voltage is 5.1 V.

Next put resistors of progressively smaller value across the output (e.g. 1 kΩ, 470 Ω, 100 Ω, 47 Ω) and observe the output voltage and ammeter reading. Notice that the voltage and the current drawn from the supply remain substantially the same until the current taken by the load resistor exceeds the 'no-load current' through the diode. Once the diode ceases to conduct in the reverse direction, the output voltage falls.

The current-limiting resistor must be sufficiently large that the maximum power rating of the Zener diode (in this case 500 mW) is not exceeded under 'no load' conditions, but this also limits the current that can be supplied to the load.

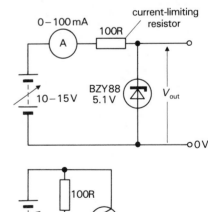

Figure 5.24   Zener diode voltage stabiliser

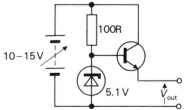

Figure 5.25   Zener stabiliser with emitter follower

Better stabilisation and higher currents can be obtained by using an emitter follower as in figure 5.25, but notice that a 5.1 V Zener diode at the input will give an output voltage of 0.6 V less (one 'diode drop'). The performance can be further improved by using a Darlington pair.

Question

15 Calculate the average power dissipated by the transistor and the average power dissipated by the loudspeaker in figure 5.27 when

(a) there is no input signal (quiescent condition);

(b) the signal amplitude is 3 V.

5.11   Output stage of an audio amplifier

The resistance of a typical loudspeaker is 8 Ω. In order to deliver an appreciable power to the loudspeaker, the output resistance of the amplifier needs to be roughly the same value. One way to achieve this low output resistance is to use an emitter follower.

To demonstrate the principle with the 2N3053, which is not a power transistor and which can only dissipate 800 mW, a 75 Ω loudspeaker should be used in the circuit of figure 5.27. The positive and negative supplies should not be greater than 5 V, or the power rating of the transistor may be exceeded. Connect an oscilloscope to display the output voltage.

First set the signal generator output voltage to zero and observe that

(a) $V_{out} = -0.6\,V$ (one 'diode drop');

(b) the transistor gets hot even when there is no signal (the *quiescent condition*), owing to a current of about 60 mA through the transistor and load.

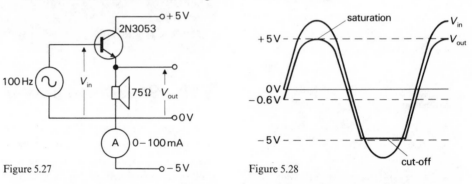

Figure 5.27   Figure 5.28

Next, slowly increase the signal generator output and observe the waveform. It will be a faithful replica of the input, shifted down one 'diode drop', until the amplitude reaches the supply voltages, when the transistor will saturate at the top and cut off at the bottom (see figure 5.28). Notice also that there is little change in the average current. This type of operation is called class A amplification.

Two disadvantages of this circuit are that

(a) power is dissipated in the transistor and loudspeaker, whether or not there is a signal;

(b) the a.c. signal to the loudspeaker is superimposed on a constant current of about 60 mA.

5.12   Class B push–pull amplifier output stage

Set up the circuit in figure 5.29, which will require a *pnp* transistor with similar parameters to the 2N3053, such as the BFX88 (which has the same pin connections as the 2N3053). The purpose of this circuit is to avoid the disadvantages of class A operation. It consists of two emitter followers: one for positive half-cycles and the other for negative half-cycles.

Observe the output voltage for input amplitudes increasing from zero to 6 V and notice the following points:

(a) For input amplitudes between 0 and 0.6 V, the current through the transistor is zero and the output voltage is zero (dead zone).

(b) For input amplitudes between 0.6 and 5 V, the output voltage has a waveform similar to figure 5.30, with pronounced crossover distortion.

(c) For input amplitudes greater than 5 V, the output voltage saturates at the top and bottom.

(d) Even with large signals, the transistors do not get hot.

Crossover distortion arises because of the 0.6 V required in either direction before one or other of the emitter followers will conduct. It is clearly unacceptable in audio amplification and must be eliminated. One way of reducing crossover distortion,

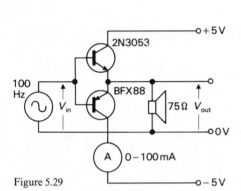

Figure 5.29

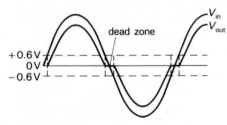

Figure 5.30   Output waveform showing crossover distortion

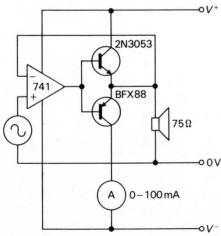

Figure 5.31

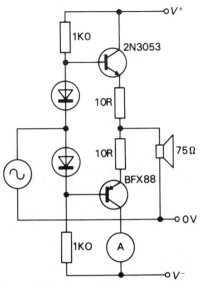

Figure 5.32

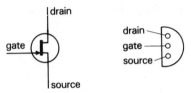

Figure 5.33   Conventional symbol for an
n-channel JFET and underside view of 2N3819

using a 741 op-amp and negative feedback, is shown in figure 5.31. You should set up this circuit to see how effective it is and satisfy yourself that you understand how it works. Notice that crossover distortion is still present to a small extent and gets worse as the frequency is increased to 10 kHz. This is because the *slew rate* of the 741 is not fast enough.

A better solution is shown in figure 5.32. Here the two transistors are biased by the two diodes so that when there is no signal both the transistors just conduct to give a quiescent current of about 1 mA. The two 10 Ω resistors are included so that if the quiescent current is too big the base–emitter voltage is reduced, thus reducing the quiescent current (negative feedback). Set up the circuit to show that it gives no crossover distortion at any audio frequency.

5.13   The junction field-effect transistor

The bipolar junction transistor has the disadvantage that it requires a small current to control it. A *field-effect transistor* (usually called an FET) is a device which controls a current by the application of a voltage. The current drawn by its input is usually negligible (about 10^{-9} A or less). One type of FET is an n-channel junction field-effect transistor (JFET). A typical example is the 2N3819.

The transfer characteristic of a JFET

Set up the circuit in figure 5.34, vary the gate–source voltage V_{gs} from 0 to -5 V and measure the drain current I_d, in order to plot a graph similar to figure 5.35. The purpose of the microammeter in the gate circuit is to demonstrate that the gate current is much less than 1 µA. The characteristic demonstrates that a change in the drain current is controlled by a change in the negative gate–source voltage. The performance of an FET can be expressed by the gradient of the transfer characteristic, and this is called the *transconductance*, which is measured in mA V^{-1}, or mS.

$$\text{Transconductance} = \frac{\Delta I_d}{\Delta V_{gs}}$$

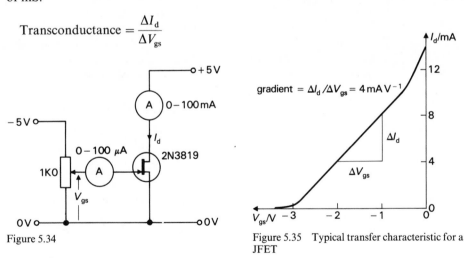

Figure 5.34

Figure 5.35   Typical transfer characteristic for a JFET

5.14   The source follower circuit

Earlier in this chapter you studied the emitter follower. It was introduced because it is a circuit with a low output resistance so that it is capable of supplying large currents, and a comparatively high input resistance so that only small currents are required to drive it. The source follower, like the emitter follower, is a resistance-matching device, but its input resistance is very much higher. It is therefore suitable for use when no current may be drawn from a signal source (e.g. an oscilloscope input).

Set up the circuit in figure 5.36 and you will see that the variations in output voltage follow the variations in input voltage, but are a volt or two more positive. This behaviour is summarised in the graph in figure 5.37.

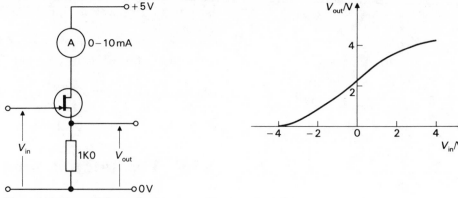

Figure 5.36   Source follower circuit   Figure 5.37

The action of the circuit is similar to the emitter follower. If the input voltage increases, the gate–source voltage increases, the drain current increases, and a larger voltage appears across the resistor. This tends to reduce the gate–source voltage, producing a negative feedback action which keeps the voltage gain of the circuit just under unity.

5.15   Further questions

These questions are about standard circuits that you are likely to meet in electronics literature.

1 A full-wave rectifying circuit is shown in figure 5.38. Draw graphs of the input voltage waveform and the output voltage waveform, using the same axes. Explain how the circuit works.

2 Two diodes can be used to protect a moving-coil meter from overload (see figure 5.39). A typical meter has a resistance of 1 kΩ and gives full-scale deflection for a current of 100 µA. Explain the action of the circuit.

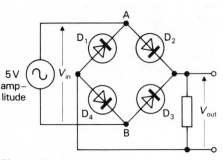

Figure 5.38   Full-wave rectifier

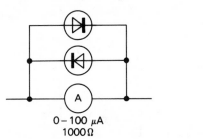

Figure 5.39   Diode protection of a meter

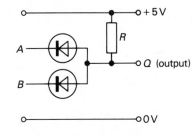

Figure 5.40   Diode logic gate

3 Figure 5.40 represents a diode logic gate. The inputs, A and B, can be at +5 V (logic 1) or 0 V (logic 0). Write down the truth table for the gate, explaining your reasoning, and state what type of gate it is.

4 A voltage doubler circuit is shown in figure 5.41. It produces a d.c. output voltage which is twice the amplitude of the a.c. input voltage. Explain how the circuit works.

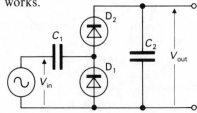

Figure 5.41   Voltage doubler circuit

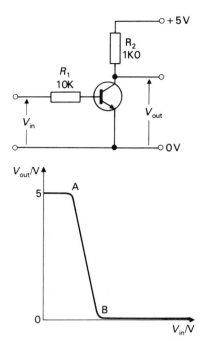

Figure 5.42   Transistor voltage amplifier

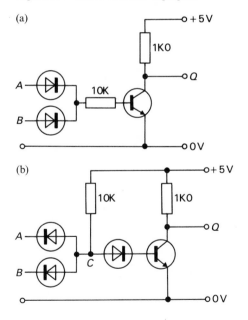

Figure 5.44   Diode–transistor logic gates

(a)

(b)

5 Figure 5.42 shows a transistor voltage amplifier circuit and its transfer characteristic. The transistor has a d.c. current gain $h_{FE} = 100$.
  (a) What is the input voltage at point A on the graph, where the transistor starts to conduct?
  (b) Calculate the collector current at point B, when the transistor is just saturated.
  (c) Calculate the base current at point B.
  (d) Calculate the input voltage at point B.
  (e) Calculate the voltage gain of the circuit over the range AB.

6 Figure 5.43 shows a circuit called a Darlington pair. Assume that the current gain of each transistor is 150.
  (a) What is the current gain of the combination?
  (b) How is the gain achieved?
  (c) What voltage is required at the input before the transistor will conduct?

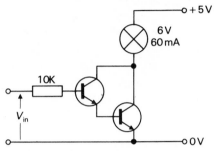

Figure 5.43   Darlington pair

7 Design a circuit which will operate a relay when a light-dependent resistor's resistance falls to about 4000 Ω. Assume a power supply of 5 V, a relay requiring 100 mA at 5 V to operate, and a transistor with $h_{FE} = 100$.

8 Two circuits for diode–transistor logic gates are shown in figure 5.44. Work out the mode of operation of each and their truth tables.

9 A bistable circuit using transistors is shown in figure 5.45. Explain how it works.

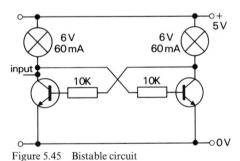

Figure 5.45   Bistable circuit

10 An astable circuit using transistors is shown in figure 5.46. Explain how it works.

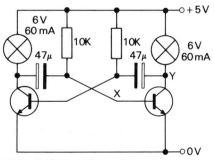

Figure 5.46   Astable circuit

6 Basic radio reception

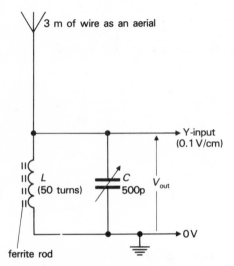

Figure 6.1   A tuned circuit

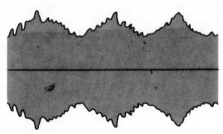

Figure 6.2

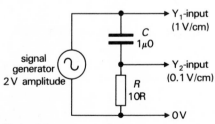

Figure 6.4

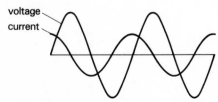

Figure 6.5

6.1   Receiving and selecting a radio signal

Set up the circuit in figure 6.1 with the oscilloscope time base set to 1 μs/cm. The coil can be made by winding ordinary 0.6 mm plastic-covered wire on a former around an 8 mm ferrite rod. If you vary the capacitance of the variable capacitor you will notice that sine waves appear on the oscilloscope screen at a few particular settings of the capacitor. You will notice a similar effect if you push the ferrite rod slowly in and out of the coil. The oscillations you observe have *radio frequencies* (r.f.) of around 1 MHz. Each sine wave is a radio signal from a different radio station and this circuit which selects them is called a *tuned circuit*.

Now select the signal with the largest amplitude and then switch the time base to 1 ms/cm. The signal should now look similar to figure 6.2. The individual oscillations are now too cramped-up to be seen, but you will notice that the *amplitude* of the oscillations is varying at *audio* frequencies (a.f.) in an irregular way. The audio signal is 'sitting on the back' of the radio frequency wave. This is called *amplitude modulation* (a.m.) of a radio frequency *carrier wave*.

A radio receiver has the following functions to perform:
(a) Select and amplify an amplitude-modulated radio frequency carrier wave.
(b) Separate the audio frequency signal from the carrier (called *demodulation*).
(c) Amplify the audio frequency signal to feed it into a loudspeaker.

This is summarised in figure 6.3. Before building a simple radio receiver you should first study the behaviour of capacitors and coils (called *inductors*) in a.c. circuits.

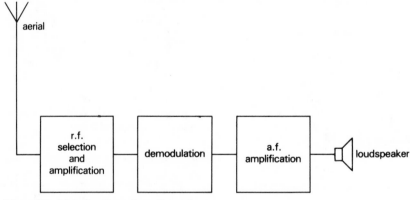

Figure 6.3   Main functions of a radio receiver

You will need a double-beam oscilloscope for some of the experiments in this chapter.

6.2   A capacitor in an a.c. circuit

One of the useful properties of a capacitor is that it 'blocks' d.c., but 'passes' a.c. You can demonstrate this by setting up the circuit in figure 6.4. The purpose of the 10 Ω resistor is to enable you to display the current in the circuit on the oscilloscope, as well as the voltage across the capacitor (see figure 6.5). For frequencies of 250, 500 and 1000 Hz, measure the amplitudes of the oscilloscope traces, to obtain the amplitudes of the voltage across the capacitor, V_0, and the current through it, I_0. (I_0 can be found by dividing the amplitude of the voltage across the resistor by its resistance, $10\,\Omega$.) Confirm the following points:

(a) The current is proportional to the frequency.

(b) The current and voltage across the capacitor are not in phase: the current 'leads' the voltage by a phase angle of $90°$.

(c) The ratio V_0/I_0 equals $1/2\pi fC$. This ratio is called the *impedance* of the capacitor to a.c., and is measured in ohms: it is inversely proportional to frequency. The variation of impedance with frequency is the property we shall use in this chapter. The impedance of a $1\,\mu F$ capacitor at $1\,kHz$ is

$$Z = \frac{1}{2\pi fC} = \frac{1}{2\pi \times 10^3 \times 10^{-6}} = 160\,\Omega$$

Question

1 Calculate the impedance of a $0.01\,\mu F$ capacitor at $1600\,Hz$, also at 200 and $6400\,Hz$. At what frequency would it have an impedance of $1\,k\Omega$?

6.3 A high-pass filter circuit

A circuit which will pass high frequencies and *attenuate* (i.e. cut down) low frequencies is called a *high-pass filter*. Set up the circuit in figure 6.6. An input voltage of $2\,V$ amplitude is convenient. Start with a frequency of $100\,Hz$. Double the frequency eight times, up to $25\,600\,Hz$. You will observe that at the lower frequencies the output voltage doubles each time the frequency doubles. At higher frequencies, the output voltage becomes constant and equal to the value of the input. The change in behaviour occurs around $1600\,Hz$, where the impedance of the capacitor becomes equal to that of the resistor. The results are summarised in figure 6.7. This type of plot is called the *frequency response* of the circuit.

It is not difficult to understand how the circuit works in principle. The capacitor and resistor work together as a potential divider. At $200\,Hz$ the impedance of the capacitor is $80\,k\Omega$, which is eight times larger than the resistor, so the output voltage across the resistor is small (i.e. attenuated). At $6400\,Hz$ the impedance of the capacitor is $2.5\,k\Omega$, which is a quarter of the value of the resistor, so the output is little different from the input (i.e. the signal passes without attenuation). A more complete and accurate analysis will be found in most A level physics textbooks, under the heading 'a.c. theory'.

This circuit is particularly useful when *coupling* various electronic stages together as you will be doing later in this chapter. For example, if an a.c. signal is fed into a source follower circuit (figure 5.36), the output will have a d.c. voltage of about $2\,V$ added to an alternating signal. By passing the output from the source follower through the high-pass filter of figure 6.6, the d.c. component (which has zero frequency) will be removed completely. The alternating component will pass virtually unchanged if it has a frequency greater than $1\,kHz$.

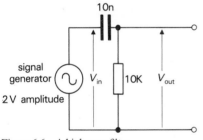

Figure 6.6 A high-pass filter

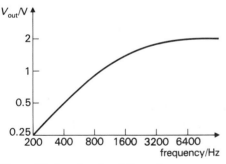

Figure 6.7 Log–log plot of V_{out} against frequency

Question

2 Sketch a frequency response for the circuit in figure 6.8. At what frequency would the output voltage be about one-eighth of the input? Suggest a name for this circuit.

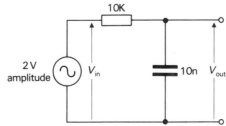

Figure 6.8

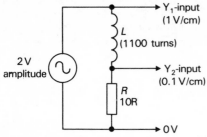

Figure 6.9

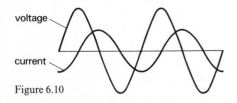

Figure 6.10

6.4   An inductor in an a.c. circuit

The coil required for this section has 1100 turns.*

The behaviour of an inductor is the 'opposite' in many ways to that of a capacitor, as you can demonstrate with the circuit of figure 6.9. For frequencies of 1, 2 and 4 kHz, measure the amplitudes of the oscilloscope traces (which will be similar to those in figure 6.10) and confirm the following points:

(a) The current is inversely proportional to the frequency.
(b) The current 'lags' the voltage by a phase angle of 90°.
(c) The impedance of the inductor, V_0/I_0, is proportional to frequency. The impedance of an inductor is given by the formula

$$Z = 2\pi fL$$

where L is the inductance in henries. You should show from your measurements that the impedance of the inductor at 1 kHz is 160 Ω, which is the same as the impedance of a 1 μF capacitor at 1 kHz.

Two ways of increasing the inductance are adding an iron or a ferrite core, or increasing the number of turns.

> **Question**
>
> **3** If the impedance of an inductor is 160 Ω at 1 kHz, calculate the inductance. What would the impedance be at 500 Hz? What would the impedance be at zero frequency (i.e. d.c.)?

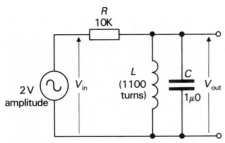

Figure 6.11

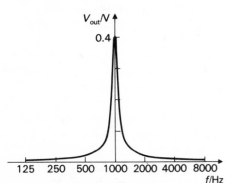

Figure 6.12   Resonance curve

6.5   Resonance in a parallel *LC* circuit

In section 6.1 you saw that a capacitor and inductor in parallel were able to select a single radio frequency. In this section you demonstrate this effect at much lower frequencies by using larger values of capacitance and inductance.

Set up the circuit in figure 6.11 and vary the frequency between 500 and 2000 Hz. You will notice that the output voltage is very much less than the input over most of the range, but that there is a sharp peak at 1000 Hz. At this frequency the circuit is said to *resonate*. The circuit selects signals close to 1000 Hz and rejects all others (see figure 6.12).

Resonance occurs because at 1000 Hz both the capacitor and the inductor have the same impedance, of 160 Ω. Since the voltage across both components is the same (V_{out}), the magnitude of the current through each of them is the same. But the current leads the voltage by 90° for a capacitor and lags the voltage by 90° for an inductor, so the currents in the capacitor and inductor are 180° out of phase. The current taken from the supply is the sum of these two currents. So in theory, the total current through the combination is zero (see figure 6.13), producing a high impedance. In practice, there is a small current.

The *LC* combination and the resistor act as a potential divider. At resonance, when the impedance of the *LC* combination is large, V_{out} is large. A small change in frequency away from resonance produces a substantial drop in the output voltage, because the sum of the currents through the capacitor and the inductor is no longer zero, and the impedance of the combination is reduced.

In general, for resonance, the impedances of the capacitor and inductor are equal, i.e.

$$\frac{1}{2\pi fC} = 2\pi fL$$

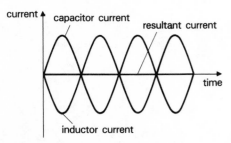

Figure 6.13

* This is the same coil as used in the Nuffield Advanced Physics course.

Rearranging the equation gives the resonant frequency:

$$f = \frac{1}{2\pi\sqrt{(LC)}}$$

You should verify for yourself that:

(a) Changing the capacitance from 1 µF to 0.01 µF changes the resonant frequency from 1 kHz to 10 kHz.

(b) Putting a resistor of 1 kΩ in parallel with the LC combination substantially lowers the output voltage at resonance.

6.6 Amplitude modulation of a carrier wave

For this section you will need a signal generator with an amplitude-modulation input (if one is not available, use the circuit described below). For this demonstration, the frequency of the carrier is only 10 kHz, instead of a radio frequency of 1 MHz or more.

Set up the circuit in figure 6.14 and display the following voltages with the oscilloscope time base set to 0.2 ms/cm:

(a) the 1 kHz signal V_1;

(b) the 10 kHz signal V_2, with the amplitude of the 1 kHz signal set to zero;

(c) the 10 kHz signal V_2, with the amplitude of the 1 kHz signal adjusted so that the oscilloscope trace is similar to the curve in figure 6.15. Observe how the 1 kHz signal is 'carried' by the 10 kHz carrier signal.

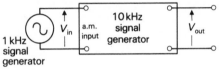

Figure 6.14

Figure 6.15

A signal generator with amplitude modulation

A 555 timer chip can be used in combination with a tuned circuit to produce an approximate sine wave using the circuit in figure 6.16. The 10 kΩ variable resistor has to be adjusted to give the maximum output voltage; this adjusts the frequency of the 555 timer to the resonant frequency of the tuned circuit. Amplitude modulation is obtained by varying the power supply to the IC.

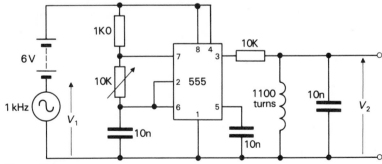

Figure 6.16

6.7 Demodulation

In order to make use of the audio signal, which modulates the higher-frequency carrier, it has to be separated from the carrier. This process of demodulation can be achieved by rectifying and smoothing the carrier. Set up the circuit in figure 6.17 with

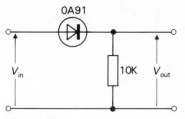

Figure 6.17

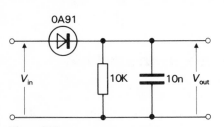

Figure 6.19

Figure 6.20

Figure 6.18

the modulated carrier from section 6.6 connected to the input. The output voltage will be a half-wave rectified version of the carrier, similar to figure 6.18.

Now add a 0.01 μF capacitor in parallel with the resistor, as in figure 6.19. The output will change to one like figure 6.20, which is a jagged copy of the 1 kHz audio signal superimposed on top of a steady d.c.

The time constant of the RC circuit needs to be short compared with the period of the audio signal, so that the output follows the audio signal faithfully. At the same time, it needs to be long compared with the period of the carrier, so that the capacitor does *not* discharge appreciably between cycles, producing the jagged effect you have observed. In this particular case,

the time constant $= RC = 10^4 \times 10^{-8} = 10^{-4}$ s

the period of the audio signal $= \dfrac{1}{10^3} = 10^{-3}$ s

the period of the carrier $= \dfrac{1}{10^4} = 10^{-4}$ s

The period of the carrier is the same as the time constant. An acceptable output would be obtained if the carrier frequency were increased to 100 kHz or more. Check this for yourself if you are using a variable-frequency signal generator to produce the carrier.

6.8 Construction of a simple radio receiver

You are now in a position to construct a simple radio receiver using circuits from chapters 4, 5 and 6. Try the one in figure 6.21.

A circuit which overcomes some of the disadvantages of figure 6.21, and which demonstrates a number of principles discussed in this book, is shown in figure 6.22. Set it up. Tune in to a strong signal. Follow the signal through the circuit by displaying the voltages at U, V, W, X, Y and Z on an oscilloscope with the time base set to 1 ms/cm, observing carefully what happens at each stage. It is better not to connect the oscilloscope directly to the tuned circuit because it alters the tuning.

Questions

4 List some of the disadvantages of the circuit in figure 6.21.

5 Suggest reasons for the addition of
(a) the FET circuit,
(b) the R_2C_2 circuit,
(c) the R_4C_4 circuit, and
(d) the push–pull circuit, in figure 6.22.

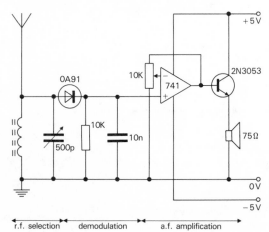

Figure 6.21

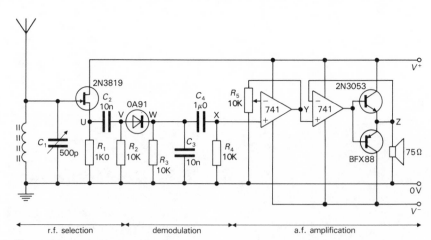

Figure 6.22

7 Further digital circuits

7.1 Introduction

The basic building blocks for most circuits in this chapter have already been described in chapters 1 to 3. The 555 timer circuits from chapter 8 will also be found useful here. In section 3.6, the binary counter was studied as a string of T flip-flops. In this chapter, the *shift register* is introduced as a string of D flip-flops. One example of its use – the *serial adder* – is followed by some circuit designs that use counters. Finally, combinations of gates are used to activate counters in examples that have been chosen to stimulate ideas for project work. An optical method of interfacing experiments to digital systems and the *7-segment* LED display are also included here.

7.2 Shift registers

A shift register is a device for temporarily storing binary information. It is used extensively for the transfer of data in computer systems. There are four types of shift register, depending on how the information is entered and retrieved from the register: serial-in serial-out (SISO), parallel-in parallel-out (PIPO), serial-in parallel-out (SIPO) and parallel-in serial-out (PISO).

A shift register is a string of flip-flops, with one bit of data stored by each flip-flop. D flip-flops are used; alternatively, JK flip-flops can be used as D flip-flops. (Figure 3.15 showed that a JK flip-flop behaved as a D type when J and K were different. This condition can be ensured for the first flip-flop in the string by connecting J and K through a NOT gate, as in figure 7.1. Subsequent flip-flops in the string do not require NOT gates for serial-in (SI) registers, because their J and K inputs are connected to Q and $\bar{Q}$ from the previous flip-flop, which will always be different.)

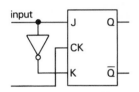

is equivalent to

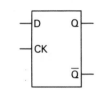

Figure 7.1

Figure 7.2

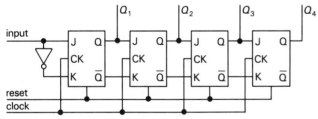

(a) Shift register of *JK* flip-flops

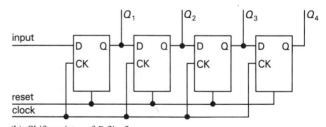

(b) Shift register of *D* flip-flops

Construct the shift register from four JK flip-flops (figure 7.2(a)) **S, 2 × 7476, 7404, I** **S, 2 × 4027, 4069, I** or from four D flip-flops (figure 7.2(b)) **S, 2 × 7474, I** **S, 2 × 4013, I** The clock pulses must come from a debounced switch. The four outputs Q_1 to Q_4 are connected to the four-LED display **I**. For CMOS ICs, all set inputs must be grounded.

Clear the register by putting the TTL reset to logic 0 or the CMOS reset to logic 1. Put the input to logic 1 and give one clock pulse. Check whether the register clocks on the rising or the falling edge of the pulse. Now return the input to logic 0. Clock three more pulses. The logic 1 has shifted to Q_4 (see figure 7.3). To fill the register, you set the input to either logic 1 or 0 before each of the first four clock pulses. This is the *serial-in* register. Reading the four LEDs together is using it as a *parallel-out* register. The next four clock pulses will clear the register with the input at 0. If you observe

pulse number	Q_1	Q_2	Q_3	Q_4
0	0	0	0	0
1	1	0	0	0
2	0	1	0	0
3	0	0	1	0
4	0	0	0	1

Figure 7.3

Questions

1 How would you make a divide-by-ten ring counter?

2 Design a device, the output of which changes every tenth input pulse, i.e. for which the output pulse is ten times the length of the input pulses.

3 Why is the Möbius counter so called?

only Q_4 as the Qs shift through, you are using a *serial-out* register. Note that for a 4-bit number, Q_1 is the most significant bit (MSB) and Q_4 the least significant bit (LSB). For the counter in figure 3.17, Q_A was the LSB and Q_D the MSB. In the shift register, you clock all the flip-flops together, unlike the ripple counter where flip-flops are clocked in sequence.

Start again with the register cleared. Connect the input to Q_4 instead of to an input switch. Use the preset to the first flip-flop to make $Q_1 = 1$. Now operate the clock repeatedly. This is a *ring counter* or divide-by-four unit.

Clear the register again. Change the input connection from Q_4 to $\bar{Q}_4$. Operate the clock repeatedly. This is a *Möbius* or *twisted-ring counter*. Make a table of the output sequence Q_1 to Q_4 similar to figure 7.3.

7.3. Serial addition

In section 2.5, you used the 4-bit parallel adder IC in figure 2.16 for addition, subtraction and multiplication. A single full adder with two shift registers and a 1-bit register will act as a *serial adder* when connected together as shown in figure 7.4.

Set up the circuit shown, using either *JK* flip-flops S, 5 × 7476, 7404, 74283, I S, 5 × 4027, 4069, 4008, I or *D* flip-flops S, 5 × 7474, 74283, I   S, 5 × 4013, 4008, I Use the first section of the 4-bit adder IC. Then S_2 will act as C_{out} if A_2 and B_2 are grounded (see figure 2.16). Add any two binary numbers which give a sum of 1111 (decimal 15) or less by entering them into the two shift registers using the preset and reset pins. Now give four clock pulses and look at the result in register A.

At the first clock pulse, the first bits in A and B are added. The sum is fed back to the input of register A and the carry is stored in the flip-flop. At the second clock pulse, the next two bits and the carry are added, the sum being entered into register A again. After four pulses the addition is complete. You can load another number into register B and add this to the sum in register A, and so on.

This is serial addition. It is relatively slow, because it requires as many clock pulses as there are bits in the numbers to be added. Parallel addition, in which the addition is performed as soon as the information appears at the inputs, is much quicker. This is achieved by connecting a *data latch* (see section 7.5) to the input of each full adder. Then one enable pulse to these latches will cause the contents of the input registers to be added and transferred to the output one. However, the serial adder requires no latches and only one full adder, whatever the number of bits in each number, making it cheaper and simpler than the parallel adder.

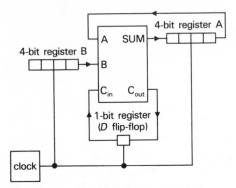

Figure 7.4   Serial adder

7.4   Sequence generators

The ripple counter is the basic device for the two examples in this section. The first is the familiar traffic lights sequence in figure 7.5. B and A are the output states of a 2-bit binary counter. Figure 7.6 shows the solution, using a box symbol for the counter.* This is not the only solution to the problem: a second one is shown in

pulse number	B	A	red	amber	green
0	0	0	0	0	1
1	0	1	0	1	0
2	1	0	1	0	0
3	1	1	1	1	0
4	0	0	0	0	1

Figure 7.5

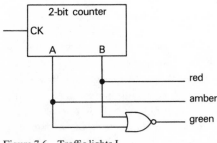

Figure 7.6   Traffic lights I

* Similar box symbols will be used for counter ICs throughout this chapter, with the connections to the reset pins labelled R. The outputs of a 4-bit counter IC are labelled A to D, and these correspond to the outputs Q_A to Q_D of the counter circuit in figure 3.17, respectively.

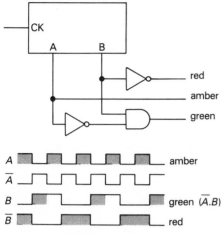

Figure 7.7 Traffic lights II

figure 7.7, together with the corresponding timing diagram for the outputs. If you make the circuit from *D* or *JK* flip-flop ICs rather than a counter IC, you can use the $\bar{Q}$ outputs to eliminate the need for NOT gates.

Allowing equal times for each light is not very realistic. The timing interval can be improved by using a 3-bit counter. Build one that will count from 0 to 7. Connect the outputs through gates to produce:

$$\text{Red} = \bar{C}$$
$$\text{Amber} = A.B$$
$$\text{Green} = C.\overline{A.B}$$

This arrangement requires only one quad two-input NAND gate IC. Using the same technique with a 4-bit counter, green and red can each be extended to seven units of time compared with one unit for amber. A three-input AND gate is required. Try it.

Questions

4 Draw the circuit for figure 7.7, excluding the NOT gates, using *D* and/or *JK* flip-flops.
5 Why is there no need for a reset for this circuit?
6 Draw the timing diagram for a 3-bit counter. Shade in areas, as in figure 7.7, to verify that the arrangement allows three units of time for red and green, compared with one unit for amber.

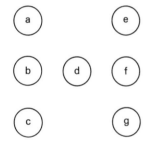

Figure 7.8 Arrangements of LEDs to simulate analogue die display

An electronic die was suggested in section 3.6. You can produce a display like that of a normal analogue die by using seven LEDs arranged as in figure 7.8. The basic design is shown in figure 7.9 using box symbols for 1-bit and 2-bit counters. (NB The reset R will have to be inverted for some TTL ICs.) The three outputs *A*, *B* and *C* will register at a rate that is dependent on the clock frequency. The output display will appear when the clock pulse is interrupted. The display will appear random, provided that the clock frequency is high enough.

The truth table for the display is given in figure 7.10. This shows that an OR and an AND gate are required. The complete circuit is shown in figure 7.11.

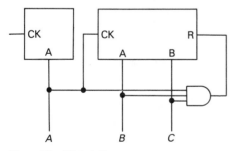

Figure 7.9 Digital die

number	C	B	A			LEDs				counter outputs required
1	0	0	1				d			A
2	0	1	0	a					g	B
3	0	1	1	a			d		g	A.B
4	1	0	0	a		c		e	g	C
5	1	0	1	a		c	d	e	g	A.C
6	1	1	0	a	b	c		e f	g	B.C
reset	1	1	1							A.B.C

Figure 7.10

Questions

7 Why does the output of figure 7.12 go low after 12 seconds if switches *A* and *B* only are open?
8 What single gate could replace the three two-input gates connected to the outputs in figure 7.12?

You can make many other devices using the counter as the basic circuit. For example, figure 7.12 shows a simple design, using TTL gates, for a timer that could be used for photographic work. The switches at the outputs of the counter will cause the gate inputs to be high if they are left open. The timer will switch off between 11 and 12 seconds if the switches at *A* and *B* are open, or between 6 and 7 seconds if only *D* is left open. The clock and the start are not synchronised so the timer only works to within one second.

An AND gate is often used as an enable, as in this circuit. You will see it again in the frequency counter of section 7.6 and in the timing circuits of section 7.7.

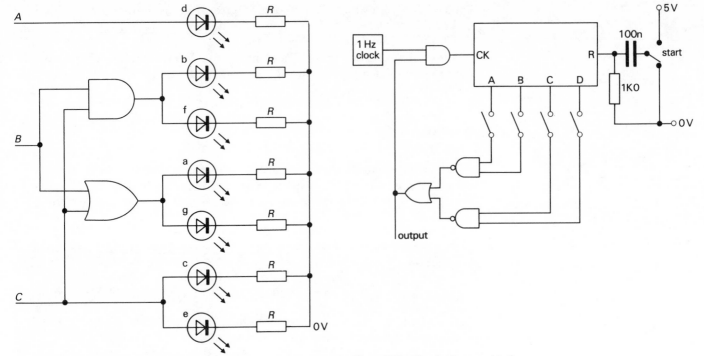

Figure 7.11   Display circuit to simulate analogue die

Figure 7.12   Simple photographic timer

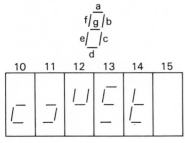

Figure 7.13

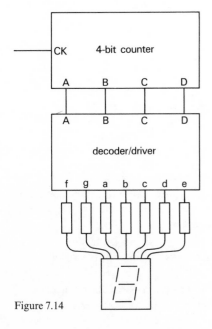

Figure 7.14

The remainder of this chapter is about number displays and counters. Instead of coupling your circuit to a TTL or CMOS counter, you may want its output to switch a relay to activate some other circuit. You can use either the circuit of figure 1.16, with the 1 kΩ load resistor replaced by the relay coil, or the emitter follower circuit of figure 5.19 for this. The relay coil must have a reverse-biased diode connected in parallel with it to protect the transistor.

7.5   The 7-segment display, decoder and data latch

The outputs of the counter circuits of section 3.6 and of the serial adder of section 7.3 were displayed in binary form on four separate LEDs. By using a *BCD to 7-segment display decoder/driver* IC, you can transform the binary code into denary and display a figure from 0 to 9. If you use a 4-bit counter rather than a decade counter with the decoder, then the display will continue to 15. The 7-segment displays for the numbers 10 to 15 are shown in figure 7.13.

Use a common anode display for TTL and a common cathode display for CMOS. A pin-out diagram for the TTL display is given in appendix II. If you are using the TTL system, connect current-limiting resistors of 270 Ω between the decoder outputs and each segment, as in figure 7.14. For simplicity, these coupling resistors will be omitted from subsequent diagrams.

You will find it difficult to mount the decoder and display ICs on the breadboard, particularly if you want a display with more than one figure. It is quite easy to make a permanent, soldered, decoder and display unit on stripboard with six flying leads to connect it to the breadboard. You will find the instructions for this in appendix II.

The *data-latch* is a PIPO shift register. It enables a reading of a rapidly-changing count to be *frozen* when required, with the counter still counting. A data latch could be used, for example, in the die circuit of figure 7.9. Instead of interrupting the clock at random intervals, you can connect the latch to the outputs *A*, *B* and *C*. Now a random clock or *enable* pulse will cause three bits of information at the inputs at that instant to pass to the output, which is displayed until the next enable pulse. A full die circuit with a 7-segment display and a data latch is shown in figure 7.15. If you are using CMOS, the counter section can be made from a single IC – either 4510 or 4516.

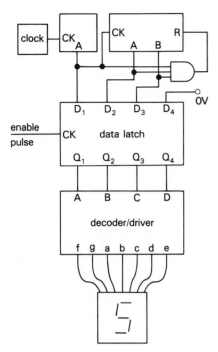

Figure 7.15   TTL digital die

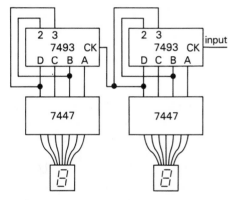

Figure 7.16   TTL counter to 99

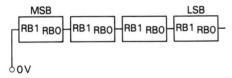

Figure 7.17   Zero-suppression connections for TTL 7447

Connect the output of the AND gate to input PE instead of R and connect input A to V^+. This will reset the counter to one.

It is straightforward to make a latch from the circuits in figure 7.2, but the number of ICs and connecting wires is becoming rather large (as shown by section 7.3), so it is more sensible to use a quad data latch IC, such as TTL 7475. The CMOS 4511 decoder already has a latch facility so no separate latch IC is required. When pin 5 goes to logic 1, the display is frozen until pin 5 returns to logic 0, when the display again follows the input changes. For TTL 7475, you must connect both pin 4 and pin 13 to logic 0 in order to freeze the display.

For counting, the most popular ICs are the TTL 7490 decade-up counter and the TTL 7493 4-bit binary counter. The nearest equivalent CMOS ICs are 4510 and 4516. (For these more elaborate ICs, the two families do not necessarily have exactly equivalent operations or controls.)

If you wish to count to 9999, for example, you will need four counter ICs, four decoders and four displays. Figure 7.16 shows a circuit for counting to 99 using TTL ICs. Further counters and decoders are coupled in the same way. The TTL decoder IC has connections that can be used to suppress unwanted zeros – so that a four-digit counter displays 470 correctly, and not as 0470, for example. The pin-out chart in appendix I shows which pins to use for this and figure 7.17 shows the arrangement of connections for a four-digit counter.

If you are using CMOS, you will find that the counter ICs have an extra input pin, the logic state of which determines whether they act as up- or down-counters. Also, external gating must be applied to the 4511 decoder in order to suppress unwanted zeros.

7.6   Frequency measurement – a tachometer

The description given below applies to a TTL circuit, but the modifications you would need to make to construct a similar circuit from CMOS ICs are quite small.

One method of measuring the speed of rotation of a motor shaft uses a disc containing a hole or a slit. This disc is attached to the shaft and rotates with it. A lamp and an opto-electronic transducer are placed so that the light beam will pass through the slit in the disc as the shaft rotates, causing electrical pulses from the transducer. Various useful transducers are shown in figure 7.18. In figure 7.18(a), V_{out} changes from logic 1 to logic 0 when the incident beam is broken. In figures 7.18(b) and (c), the transistors switch off when the beam is interrupted, causing V_{out} to rise. In figure 7.18(d), the photodiode is in reverse bias, so the leakage current falls when the

Figure 7.18

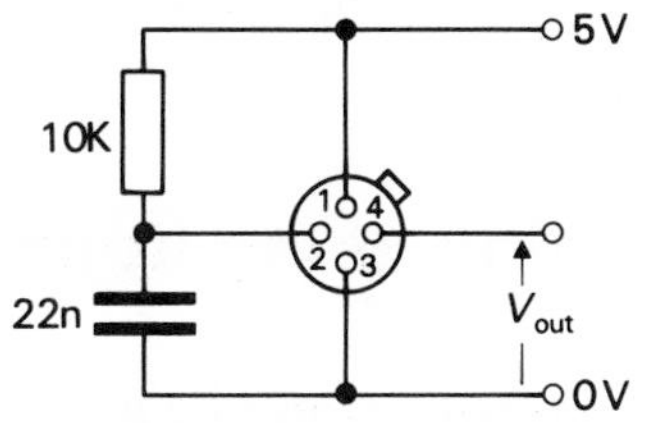

(a) Light-activated switch (RS 305–434)
(top view, i.e. pins down)

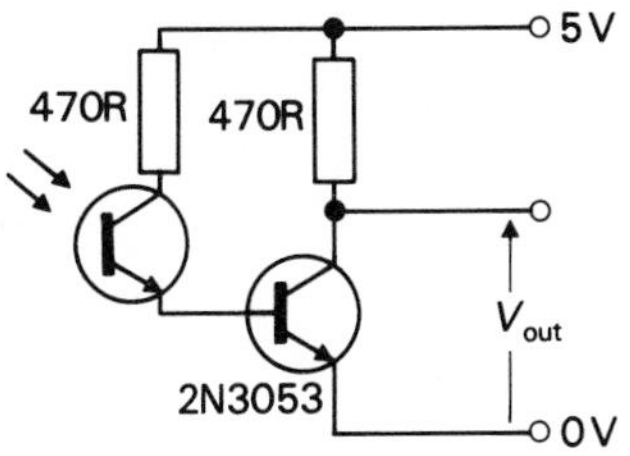

(b) Phototransistor switch

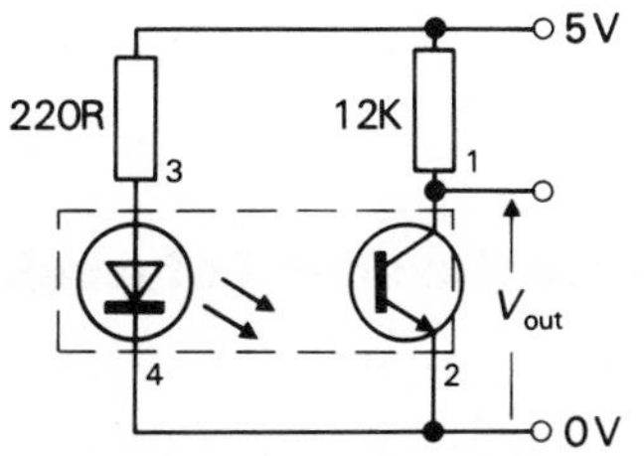

(c) Slotted opto-switch (RS 306–061)

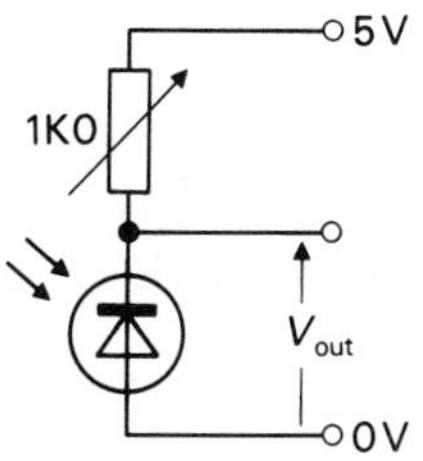

(d) Photodiode

beam is broken and V_{out} rises. The 1 kΩ variable resistor in figure 7.18(d) is adjusted so that V_{out} swings sufficiently to switch a Schmitt trigger IC. The ORP12 LDR circuits in figures 1.18, 1.19 and 5.15, which are similar to but less sensitive than these circuits, are also suitable.

The electrical pulses from these transducers may be ragged in shape and also may not change rapidly between the two logic states. By connecting a Schmitt trigger IC (TTL 7414) on the output of the transducer, an inverted square pulse will be produced. The time period of this pulse will vary, depending on the input pulse shape. By connecting the input pulses to the trigger input of the 555 timer monostable circuit (see section 8.3), the output pulses, which are not inverted, will not only be square but also of a constant time period.

Figure 7.19

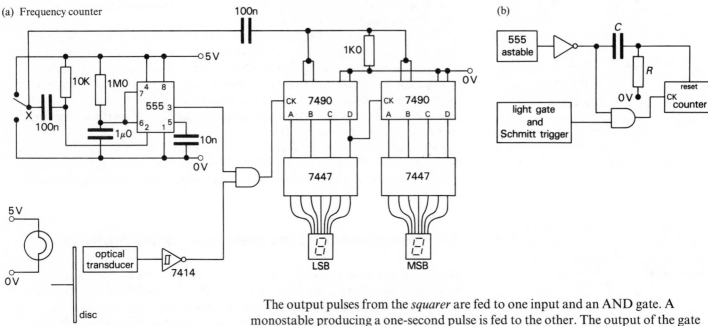

The output pulses from the *squarer* are fed to one input and an AND gate. A monostable producing a one-second pulse is fed to the other. The output of the gate acts as the clock input to a counter. Figure 7.19(a) shows the full circuit. The switch X is connected from 5 V to 0 V to take a reading and returned to 5 V to reset the counter.

The block diagram for a frequency counter that resets automatically is shown in figure 7.19(b). *The mark-to-space ratio for the 555 astable (see section 8.3) is variable*, depending on the values of R_1 and R_2 (see figure 8.5). Choose R_2 and C such that the *space* period is one second. Choose R_1 to give a reasonable time to read the display (the *mark* period), say three seconds. The small CR combination will give a rapid positive spike (see section 3.7) at the beginning of the count, resetting the counter.

Question

9 What effect does the small *RC* combination have when the enabling pulse falls from logic 1 to logic 0?

7.7   Timing using light gates

To measure the speed of a vehicle using a single gate

While the vehicle passes in front of the lamp, and the light is blocked, the input to the AND gate is at logic 1 (see figure 7.20). The clock pulses are counted during this period. Knowing the length of the vehicle, it is possible to calculate its average speed as it passed the gate.

To measure the speed of a vehicle between two gates

At reset (figure 7.21), $B = 0$, so AND gate 1 is enabled. The first pulse, as the vehicle crosses light gate 1, triggers the 2-bit counter. The output A enables AND gate 2. The clock pulses are counted until the second pulse, when the second beam is broken,

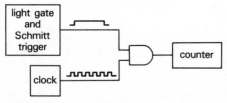

Figure 7.20   Pulse-length counter

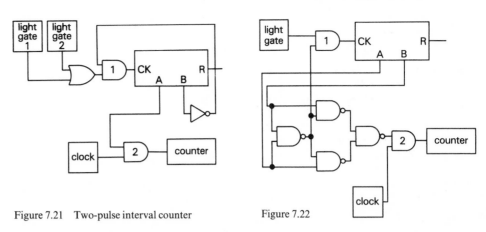

Figure 7.21   Two-pulse interval counter   Figure 7.22

which changes output A to 0 (disabling AND gate 2) and output B to 1. AND gate 1 is disabled, so further pulses will not alter the counter until the reset is activated.

Questions

10 Simplify the circuit in figure 7.21 by converting the OR gate, AND gate 1 and the NOT gate to two NOR gates.

11 Should the 2-bit control counter be triggered on its rising edge for these circuits?

To measure the time of a pendulum swing

At reset (figure 7.22), A and B are 0 so the output to the first NAND gate is 1, enabling AND gate 1. Pulse 1, as the pendulum crosses the light beam, makes $A = 1$ and $B = 0$; pulse 2 makes $A = 0$ and $B = 1$; pulse 3 makes $A = 1$ and $B = 1$. The four NAND gates act as an EOR gate, so the output enables AND gate 2 until pulse 3, when the pendulum has completed one swing. The counter is frozen at pulse 3. AND gate 1 is disabled because the output to the first NAND gate is 0. The 2-bit counter must be reset to re-activate the system.

Clock circuits

Figure 7.23 shows a simple clock which will give a 100 Hz output. By adding a 7490 IC (a decade counter) to its output, it can be converted to a 0.1-second clock (see figure 7.24).

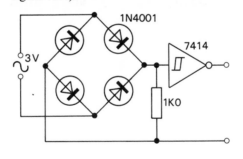

Figure 7.23   100 Hz clock

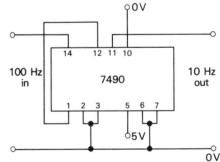

Figure 7.24   Add-on for 10 Hz clock

7.8   Further questions

1 The outputs of the 4-bit binary counter (figure 3.17) are labelled Q_A, Q_B, Q_C and Q_D. Use the eight flip-flop outputs Q_A, $\bar{Q}_A$, Q_B, $\bar{Q}_B$, etc. and ten four-input AND gates to design a *BCD-to-decimal decoder*.

2 Design a device to time the interval between two pulses. Assume that the interval is at least one minute and that the accuracy required is to the nearest second, i.e. the interval could be measured by counting the flashes of an LED.

3 Design a circuit which will cause an LED to light if two pulses are detected within one second of each other (a *coincidence detector*). How can the circuit be modified to change the time interval between the pulses that will cause the LED to light?

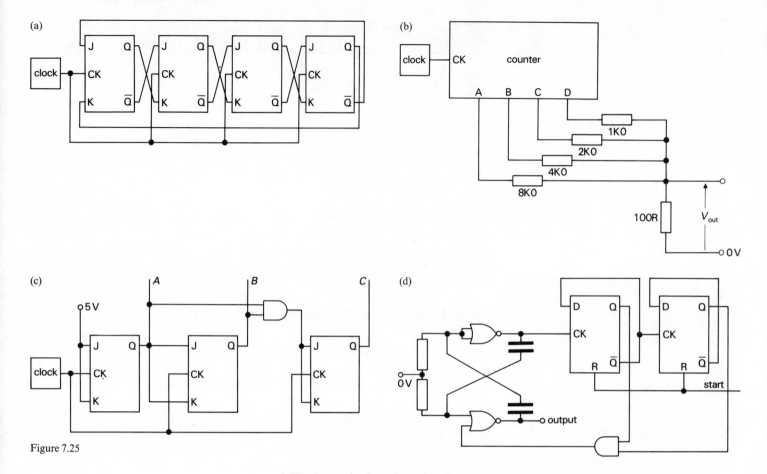

Figure 7.25

4 Work out the function of each of the circuits in figure 7.25.

5 Design a circuit to produce and count square pulses. Assume that you have an operational amplifier, a $\pm 15\,\text{V}$ power supply, a transistor, a suitable Zener diode, a diode, resistors, capacitors, and a TTL counter and display. (Use circuits from chapters 3, 4 and 5 as building blocks.)

8 Further analogue systems

8.1 Introduction

Chapter 4 introduced the fundamental circuits of analogue systems using operational amplifiers. This chapter contains further circuits using op-amps to solve practical problems. Set them up and investigate how they behave. You should be able to explain their operation in terms of the ideas and rules introduced in chapter 4. One new chip – the 555 timer – is introduced.

The sections of this chapter describe more amplifier circuits, oscillators, digital-to-analogue conversion, power supplies, analogue computing and a simple servo mechanism.

8.2 Further amplifier circuits

Questions

1 Calculate the maximum and minimum values for the closed-loop gain in the circuit shown in figure 8.1.
2 Explain why the capacitor C_1 is necessary in the circuit shown in figure 8.3.
3 Calculate the gain of the amplifier in figure 8.3.

The performance of practical op-amp circuits is determined by the external components in them. Varying the feedback components, in particular, can lead to a wide variety of amplifiers for special purposes. For example, figure 8.1 shows a non-inverting amplifier with a potentiometer to act as a gain control.

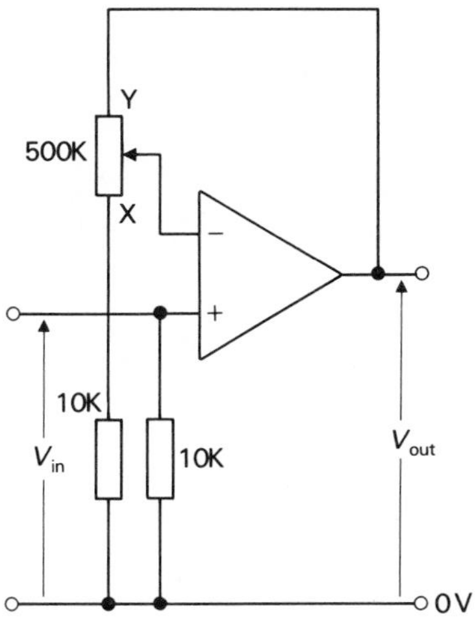

Figure 8.1

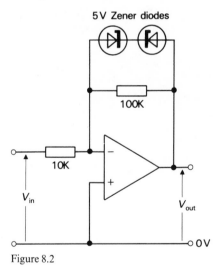

Figure 8.2

Figure 8.3

Manufacturers usually try to design linear amplifiers. However, sometimes we wish to introduce non-linearity into the output of the amplifier in a known way. Figure 8.2 shows a circuit for clipping the waveform when it rises above V_Z, the voltage at which the Zener diode starts to conduct. It could be used as a 'fuzz box' for an electric guitar. When V_{out} is less than V_Z, the circuit behaves as a linear amplifier. When V_{out} exceeds V_Z, the Zener diodes provide a low resistance path that increases the feedback signal and restricts V_{out} to $(V_Z + V_{in})$. The clipping can be made to occur at different voltages by using Zener diodes with different breakdown voltages.

All the op-amp circuits used so far require power supplies that maintain both positive (V^+) and negative (V^-) voltages with respect to zero potential. Figure 8.3 shows a circuit with a single positive power supply with respect to zero potential. It is arranged to amplify alternating signals fed in through the capacitor C_1.

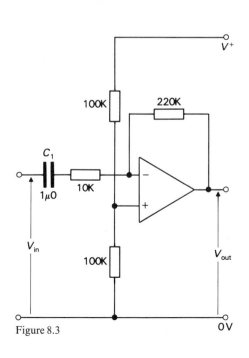

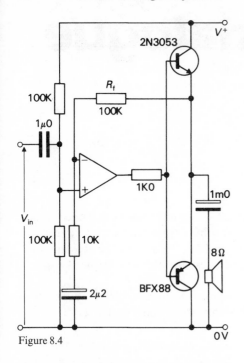

Figure 8.4

The 741 op-amp cannot deliver enough power into a load to drive a loudspeaker. To construct an audio power amplifier, a pair of transistors may be used as a current amplifier. Figure 8.4 shows a typical circuit in which a matched pair (one *pnp* and one *npn*) of transistors are fed by the op-amp and drive a loudspeaker. The feedback resistor R_f is connected to the output of the transistor amplifier so that negative feedback is applied overall to both the op-amp and the transistor current amplifier.

8.3   Timer circuits using the 555 chip

Section 4.12 introduced a simple oscillator using an op-amp. Oscillators and timers are such important building blocks of electronic systems that custom-made chips are available. One of the most popular of these is the NE 555 timer which will operate as an astable (oscillator) or monostable (pulse producer) circuit. Figure 8.5 shows the connections to the 555 chip for the astable circuit. This circuit produces a square-wave output whose frequency f is given by

$$f = \frac{1.44}{(R_1 + 2R_2)C}$$

The maximum frequency of operation is $\sim 1\,\text{MHz}$. R_1 and R_2 should not be less than $1\,\text{k}\Omega$.

We can also use the 555 chip as a monostable – a circuit that produces a single standard output pulse every time the input is triggered. Figure 8.6 shows the connections to the 555 chip for this application. The duration T of the output pulse (in seconds) is given by

$$T = 1.1\,RC$$

The pulse is triggered by the input voltage on pin 2 falling from V^+ to $0\,\text{V}$.

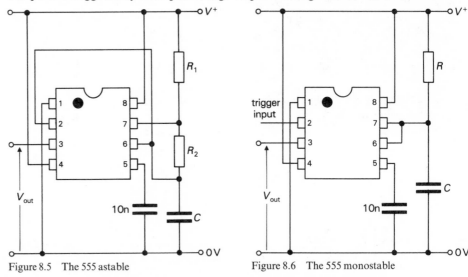

Figure 8.5   The 555 astable   Figure 8.6   The 555 monostable

8.4   A variable-frequency pulse generator

The circuit in figure 8.7 uses two 555 chips. One is a variable-frequency oscillator which triggers the second. This is a monostable which produces uniform pulses that are suitable for counting by the frequency meter.

8.5   A frequency meter

The op-amp integrator can be used to count pulses and to produce an output voltage that is proportional to the rate at which the pulses arrive at the integrator. Figure 8.8

Questions

4 Explain why the loudspeaker is connected to the output of the amplifier through a capacitor in figure 8.4.

5 The maximum value of R in figure 8.6 which gives reliable operation is $2.2\,\text{M}\Omega$. Choose values of R and C to give a circuit which produces a $0.5\,\text{s}$ pulse.

6 Calculate the range of frequencies over which the 555 astable in figure 8.7 will operate.

7 Calculate the duration of the output pulse of the 555 monostable in figure 8.7.

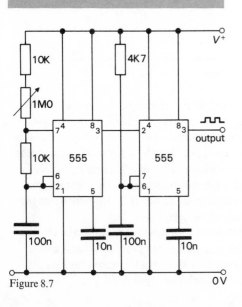

Figure 8.7

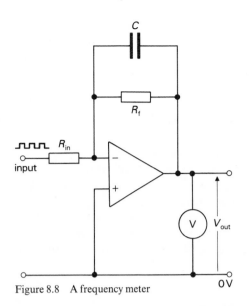

Figure 8.8   A frequency meter

shows a suitable circuit. Uniform positive pulses, from a 555 monostable, arrive at the inverting input of the op-amp. Without the feedback resistor R_f, the capacitor C would charge up and V_{out} would fall to V^-. However, R_f discharges the capacitor so that an equilibrium value of V_{out} is reached, at which the rate of arrival of pulses of charge to C balances the rate of discharge of C through R_f. A voltmeter connected to read V_{out} can be calibrated to measure the frequency of arrival of input pulses.

For example, when n pulses, each of amplitude V and duration t arrive each second, the average current in the input resistor is Vnt/R_{in}. By rule 1 (see section 4.4) this is also the current in R_f, and by rule 2 the inverting input in figure 8.8 is a virtual earth point.

Thus $$V_{out} = \frac{R_f Vnt}{R_{in}}$$

V_{out} is proportional to n. Choose suitable values for the pulse generator in figure 8.7 to produce 1 ms pulses at up to 100 pulses per second and then choose values for R_{in}, R_f and C to give a frequency meter suitable for measuring frequencies up to 100 Hz.

8.6   Triangle or sawtooth oscillators

Astable and relaxation oscillators, whether using op-amps or the 555 timer, derive their action from the charging and discharging of a capacitor. When an oscilloscope is used to observe the rise and fall of the voltage across the capacitor, a triangle waveform is seen. For a mark-to-space ratio of 1 (a square-wave output), the charging and discharging times are equal and a symmetrical waveform is seen. Figure 8.9 shows a simple circuit which uses a buffer to avoid the output loading the charging circuit of the capacitor. The frequency of the waveform is governed by the time constant RC.

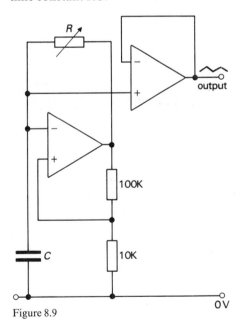

Figure 8.9

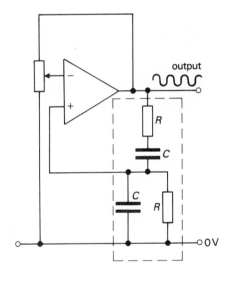

Figure 8.10   A sine-wave oscillator

8.7   Sine-wave oscillators

Most signal generators produce sine-wave outputs. We can produce square waves from these by adding a Schmitt trigger circuit to the output of the sine-wave oscillator. At audio frequencies, most sine-wave oscillators are *phase-shift oscillators*. An op-amp is given a feedback network which itself introduces a phase shift for a signal passing through. This phase shift varies with frequency.

Figure 8.10 shows an op-amp with feedback to the non-inverting input. The

Questions

8 What factors govern the choice of value of capacitor C in figure 8.8?

9 Modify the circuit in figure 8.9 to produce a sawtooth wave with a slow rise and a sharp fall in output voltage.

10 Choose values of R and C in figure 8.10 to produce a 1 kHz oscillator.

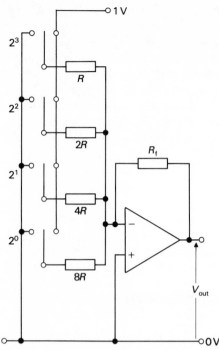

Figure 8.11   A digital-to-analogue converter

feedback components, shown within the broken line, introduce zero phase shift at only one frequency, which is given by $f = 1/2\pi RC$. Hence, at this frequency, there is positive feedback and the op-amp goes into oscillation. With this simple circuit you will need to adjust the variable resistor carefully to obtain a good sine-wave output.

8.8   Digital-to-analogue conversion

After information has been processed digitally, we may wish to convert it to an analogue output. By using the op-amp to sum voltages, we can convert binary numbers to denary and add them together. Figure 8.11 shows a simple circuit which produces an output voltage that is proportional to the denary equivalent of a 4-bit binary number. When 1 V is applied to the 2^0 input, the output voltage is $(-R_f/8R)V$. When 1 V is applied to the 2^1 input, V_{out} is $(-R_f/4R)V$, etc. Make $R = 1\,k\Omega$ and choose a suitable value of R_f so that V_{out} will cover all 4-bit binary numbers (0 to 15 in denary).

8.9   Stabilised power supplies

A simple power supply can be made by rectifying the output of a transformer connected to the mains. This is unsuitable for many electronic circuits because as the current delivered increases, the voltage between the terminals of the supply drops. Also, the supply contains an a.c. ripple. To stabilise the power supply output at a constant voltage and remove the ripple, we can use a differential op-amp as shown in figure 8.12.

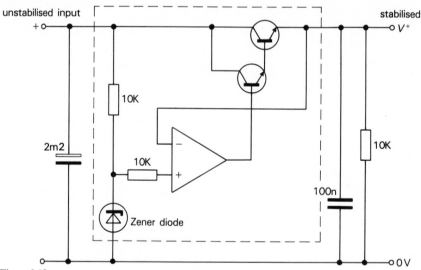

Figure 8.12

The op-amp compares the unstabilised input from the power supply with a reference voltage provided by the Zener diode. Its output controls the transistor current amplifier in series with the supply. When V_{out} changes, rule 2 states that the output voltage of the op-amp will change to restore V_{out} to its former value (which was fixed by the breakdown voltage of the Zener diode used). The input voltage must be a few volts larger than V_{out} and the transistors must carry the full-load current of the power supply. For many applications, the components within the broken line are in a single integrated circuit regulator.

8.10   Analogue computers

In chapter 4 the op-amp was used to add and subtract voltages and to integrate them

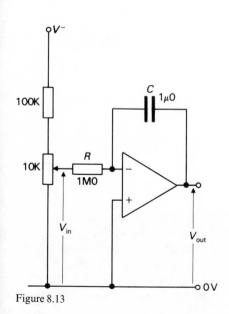

Figure 8.13

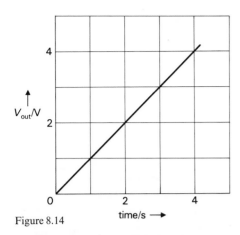

Figure 8.14

Questions

11 Sketch the oscilloscope display if V_{in} was made equal to -0.5 V. To what acceleration would this correspond?
12 Sketch the oscilloscope display with $V_{in} = -1$ V and with an initial voltage of 2 V across the capacitor when the oscilloscope trace starts, i.e. at $t = 0$. To what does the initial voltage across the capacitor correspond?

with respect to time. These mathematical operations carried out by op-amps form the basis of analogue computers.

Consider the circuit in figure 8.13. The time constant (RC) is 1 s. When V_{in} is -1 V, V_{out} rises at 1 V s^{-1}. The oscilloscope display, started when $V_{out} = 0$ (when the 1 µF capacitor is discharged), will look like figure 8.14, which is the graph of

$$V_{out} = -V_{in}t \qquad \text{where } V_{in} = -1\,\text{V} \\ \text{and } t = \text{Time}$$

Use this circuit to plot a simulated speed–time graph to represent the equation

$$\text{Speed} = \text{Acceleration} \times \text{Time}$$

Comparing these two equations, speed corresponds to V_{out}, acceleration corresponds to V_{in} and time is real time.

To convert figure 8.14 into a speed–time graph, the voltage axis needs to be scaled, as does the input voltage V_{in}. For instance, if an acceleration of $10\,\text{m s}^{-2}$ corresponds to $V_{in} = -1$ V, the change of 1 V s^{-1} in V_{out} corresponds to a $10\,\text{m s}^{-1}$ change in speed every second, and 1 V on the V_{out} axis will correspond to $10\,\text{m s}^{-1}$. Thus, the circuit computes the speed from the acceleration and time: V_{out} varies with time in the same way as the speed varies with time. The oscilloscope displays a graph with the correct time axis and the Y-axis scaled such that the deflection produced by 1 V corresponds to $10\,\text{m s}^{-1}$.

The graphical solution produced by this analogue system is not as accurate numerically as that from a digital computer. The op-amp is not an ideal op-amp, and there are manufacturing tolerances in the resistors and capacitors which define the various scaling factors. However, it does operate in real time: that is, on the same time-scale as the phenomenon it represents.

8.11 Analogue solutions of differential equations

Section 8.10 took a second look at the integrator circuit, for which

$$V_{out} = \frac{-1}{RC} \int V_{in}\,dt$$

In differential form we may write

$$V_{in} = -RC\frac{dV_{out}}{dt}$$

We will use the circuit in figure 8.15 to solve a differential equation. The op-amp acts as an integrator with two inputs, which are summed at the inverting input.

Set up the circuit shown in figures 8.15. The terminals T are for charging or discharging the capacitor to set the initial conditions. In this and in subsequent analogue computer circuits, you may need to fit and adjust an offset-null control (see appendix II).

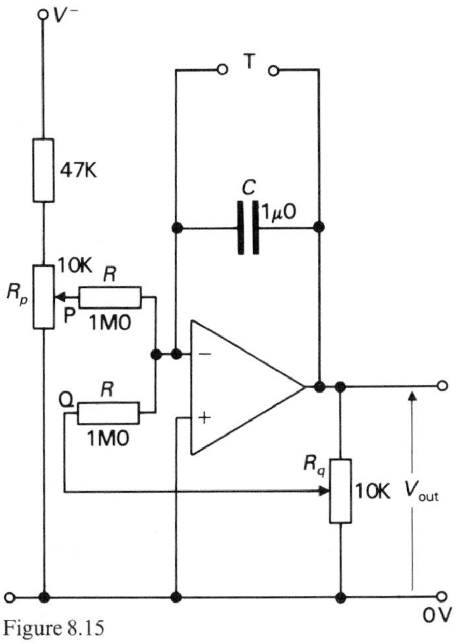

(a) Set R_q to zero and observe V_{out} using an oscilloscope with the time base set to $1\,\text{s cm}^{-1}$. Use R_p to set the voltage at P to -1 V and observe that V_{out} goes positive at 1 V s^{-1}, that is

$$\frac{dV_{out}}{dt} = 1\,\text{V s}^{-1}$$

$$= \frac{-V_{in}}{RC}$$

When the voltage at P is set to $-p$, the oscilloscope displays solutions of

$$\frac{dV_{out}}{dt} = +p$$

if the capacitor is uncharged at time $t = 0$.

Figure 8.15

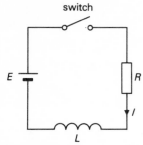

Figure 8.16

(b) Set R_p to zero and R_q such that a fraction q of V_{out} is fed back to the inverting input. The relationship between V_{in} and V_{out} is now

$$V_{in} = qV_{out}$$

$$= -RC\frac{dV_{out}}{dt}$$

$$= -\frac{dV_{out}}{dt} \quad \text{since } RC = 1\,\text{s}$$

If, at time $t = 0$, the capacitor is uncharged, $V_{out} = 0$, as does dV_{out}/dt. The oscilloscope should show $V_{out} = 0$ at all times. Charge the 1 µF capacitor by momentarily connecting a 9 V battery across terminals T, and observe the variation of V_{out} with time after the battery is disconnected.

(c) Using both potentiometers to set $-p$ (the voltage on the P input) and qV_{out} (the voltage on the Q input), gives a circuit which will follow the solution of

$$\frac{dV_{out}}{dt} = -V_{in}$$

$$= p - qV_{out}$$

For this circuit, for which $RC = 1$ s, the graphs displayed on the oscilloscope in (b) are of the form

$$V_{out} = V_0\,e^{-qt}$$

where V_0 is the initial voltage to which the 1 µF capacitor is charged. In (c), the graphs are plots of

$$V_{out} = \frac{p}{q}\left(1 - e^{-qt}\right)$$

when the 1 µF capacitor is initially uncharged.

8.12 An analogue solution of simple harmonic motion

The equation of motion for simple harmonic motion (SHM) is of the form

$$\frac{d^2x}{dt^2} = -px \quad \text{where } p \text{ is a constant}$$

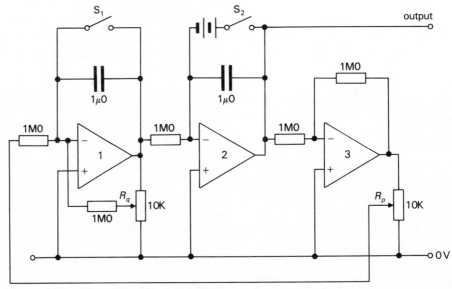

Figure 8.17   An analogue computer to solve SHM

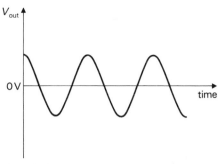

Figure 8.18

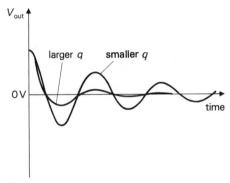

Figure 8.19

We require two successive integrations to solve a second-order differential equation like this. Since op-amp integrators also invert the signal, three op-amps are necessary for a practical arrangement – two to integrate and one to invert. Figure 8.17 shows a practical circuit. Switches S_1 and S_2 are parts of a double-pole switch. They set the initial voltages across the two capacitors. Opening them starts the cycle.

Set up the circuit and connect the output to an oscilloscope whose time base is set to $1\,\mathrm{s\,cm^{-1}}$. (Once again we make the time constant of the integrators 1 s.) Set potentiometer R_q to zero and observe that when potentiometer R_p is not set to zero, the output displays a sine wave when switches S_1 and S_2 are opened.

In operation, the input to op-amp 1 represents d^2x/dt^2. The output of op-amp 1 represents $-dx/dt$ and the output of op-amp 2, $+x$, which is connected to the oscilloscope. Op-amp 3 is an inverter with a gain of unity giving an output $-x$. R_p takes a fraction p of $-x$ and feeds it back to the input of op-amp 1. At the input to op-amp 1, therefore

$$\frac{d^2x}{dt^2} = -px$$

which is the equation for SHM. The trace observed on the oscilloscope has the form shown in figure 8.18.

Real oscillations are *damped*. The analogue computer can simulate velocity-dependent damping by linking the output of the second potentiometer R_q and its input resistor to the summing junction at the input to op-amp 1. A fraction q of $-dx/dt$ is fed back to op-amp 1 so that at its input we have

$$\frac{d^2x}{dt^2} = -q\frac{dx}{dt} - px$$

This is the equation for damped SHM. The shapes of the oscilloscope traces for this equation for large and small values of q are shown in figure 8.19.

Question

16 Modify the circuit in figure 8.17 to solve the differential equation

$$\frac{d^2x}{dt^2} = -px - k$$

8.13 Op-amps in control

Op-amps have many applications in the control of systems. Look at the circuit in figure 8.20, in which R_1 and R_2 are light-dependent resistors and M is a permanent-magnet d.c. motor. Explain how V_{out} will vary as the illumination of the light-dependent resistors varies. We can use such a circuit to make the motor move a scanner containing R_1 and R_2 so that both R_1 and R_2 remain equally illuminated even when the light source moves. A 741 op-amp will not supply a large enough current to drive a motor directly so you will need to use a transistor current amplifier. Look at the circuit in figure 8.21 and work out how to drive the motor.

8.14 A simple servo system

A closed-loop servo is a system with feedback from output to input to check that the system has carried out the instruction given to it. Figure 8.21 shows a simple position servo. R_2 is connected mechanically to the motor so that, when the motor shaft rotates, it moves the wiper contact of R_2. R_1 provides the input control voltage. When the sum of the voltages from R_1 and R_2 is zero, the output is zero and the

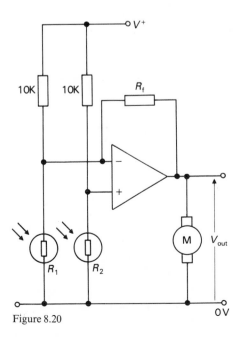

Figure 8.20

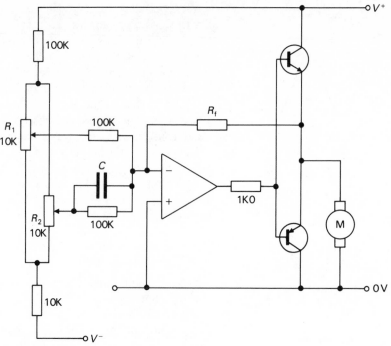

Figure 8.21

motor is at rest. A control movement altering R_1 produces an output voltage which causes the motor to rotate in the direction which alters R_2 until the sum of the voltages from R_1 and R_2 is again zero. Servos tend to overshoot the equilibrium position and then oscillate about it. We can cure this by adjusting the gain of the op-amp through the feedback resistor R_f and adding capacitor C.

8.15   Further questions

1   Figure 8.22 shows a 555 astable circuit being used to trigger a 555 monostable. Draw the outputs A and B of the astable and the monostable to scale on the same axes.

2   Figure 8.23 shows an alternative way of clipping the output of an op-amp, using silicon rectifier diodes in place of Zener diodes. Explain how this arrangement of diodes changes the waveform and sketch the output from this amplifier as a function of time when a sine-wave input of amplitude 1 V is used.

3   Draw graphs of the input and output waveforms for the op-amp circuit shown in figure 8.24 when the input waveform is
   (a) a sine wave of amplitude 1 V and frequency 50 Hz, and
   (b) a square wave of amplitude 1 V, frequency 50 Hz and a mark-to-space ratio of 1.

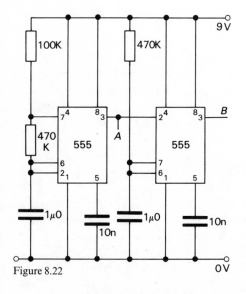

Figure 8.22

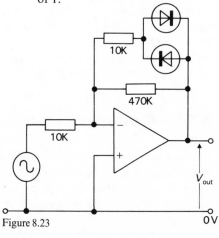

Figure 8.23

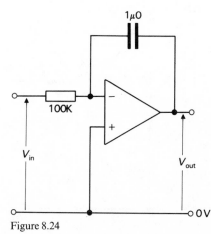

Figure 8.24

Appendix I
Pin connections

TTL (top view)

7400

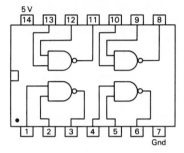

7402

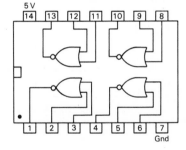

7404

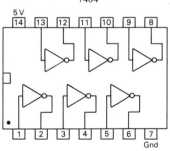

7408

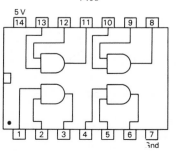

Quad two-input NAND gate

$$Y = \overline{A.B}$$

inputs		output
A	B	Y
0	0	1
0	1	1
1	0	1
1	1	0

Quad two-input NOR gate

$$Y = \overline{A + B}$$

inputs		output
A	B	Y
0	0	1
0	1	0
1	0	0
1	1	0

Hex inverter (NOT gate)

$$Y = \overline{A}$$

input	output
A	Y
0	1
1	0

Quad two-input AND gate

$$Y = A.B$$

inputs		output
A	B	Y
0	0	0
0	1	0
1	0	0
1	1	1

CMOS (top view)

4011

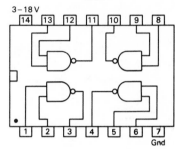

4001

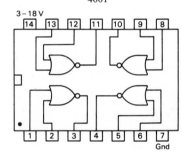

4069

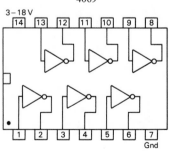

4081

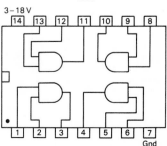

TTL (top view)

7432

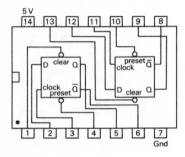

CMOS (top view)

Quad two-input OR gate

$$Y = A + B$$

inputs		output
A	**B**	**Y**
0	0	0
0	1	1
1	0	1
1	1	1

4071

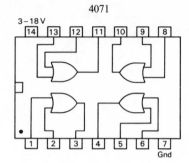

7474

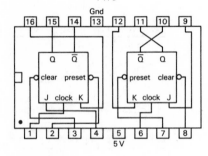

Dual *D* flip-flops

inputs				outputs	
clock	D	preset	clear	Q	$\overline{Q}$
⌐	0	1	1	0	1
⌐	1	1	1	1	0
⌐	×	1	1	no change	
×	×	1	0	0	1
×	×	0	1	1	0
×	×	0	0	1	1

inputs				outputs	
CK	D	S	R	Q	$\overline{Q}$
⌐	0	0	0	0	1
⌐	1	0	0	1	0
⌐	×	0	0	no change	
×	×	0	1	0	1
×	×	1	0	1	0
×	×	1	1	1	1

4013

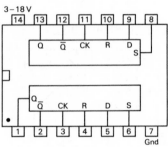

7476

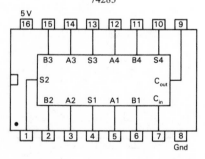

Dual *JK* flip-flops

inputs					outputs	
clock	J	K	preset	clear	Q	$\overline{Q}$
⌐	0	0	1	1	no change	
⌐	1	0	1	1	1	0
⌐	0	1	1	1	0	1
⌐	1	1	1	1	toggle	
⌐	×	×	1	1	no change	
×	×	×	1	0	0	1
×	×	×	0	1	1	0
×	×	×	0	0	1	1

inputs					outputs	
CK	J	K	S	R	Q	$\overline{Q}$
⌐	0	0	0	0	no change	
⌐	1	0	0	0	1	0
⌐	0	1	0	0	0	1
⌐	1	1	0	0	toggle	
⌐	×	×	0	0	no change	
×	×	×	1	0	1	0
×	×	×	0	1	0	1
×	×	×	1	1	1	1

4027

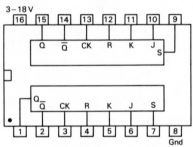

74283

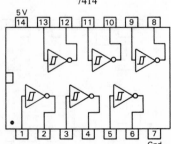

4-bit full adder with carry

All unused inputs must be grounded.

4008

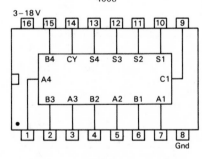

7414

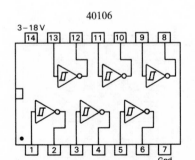

Hex inverting Schmitt trigger

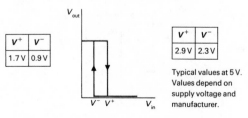

V^+	V^-
1.7 V	0.9 V

V^+	V^-
2.9 V	2.3 V

Typical values at 5 V.
Values depend on
supply voltage and
manufacturer.

'×' means 'either state'

40106

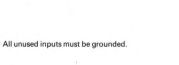

TTL (top view)

7447

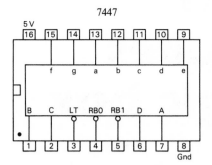

BCD to 7-segment decoder/driver

LT	RB0	RB1	action
0	1	×	all segments on
1	1	0	for zero suppression
1	1	1	outputs 0–15

LT	ST	BI	action
0	×	×	all segments on
1	0	×	continuous count
1	1	×	latches output
1	0	0	for zero suppression

CMOS (top view)

4511

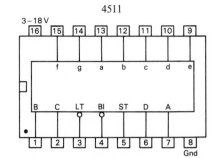

7475

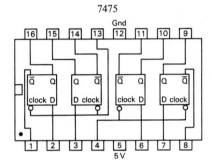

4-bit bistable data latch

inputs		outputs	
D	EN	Q	$\overline{Q}$
0	1	0	1
1	1	1	0
×	0	latch	

inputs		output
pin 5	pin 6	Q
0	0	D
0	1	latch
1	0	latch
1	1	D

4042

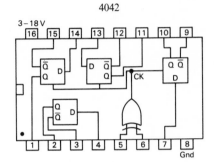

7486

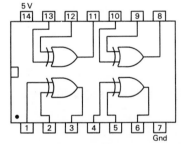

Quad two-input exclusive OR gate

$$Y = A \oplus B$$

inputs		output
A	B	Y
0	0	0
0	1	1
1	0	1
1	1	0

4070

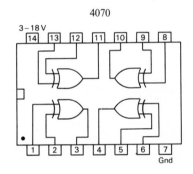

7490

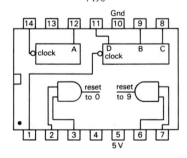

Decade counter

reset inputs				outputs			
pin 2	pin 3	pin 6	pin 7	D	C	B	A
1	1	0	×	0	0	0	0
1	1	×	0	0	0	0	0
×	×	1	1	1	0	0	1
0	×	0	×	count			
×	0	×	0	count			
0	×	×	0	count			
×	0	0	×	count			

Output A is to be connected to pin 1.

CK	R	PE	C1	U/D	action
⎍	0	0	0	1	count up
⎍	0	0	0	0	count down
	0	0	×	×	no change
×	1	×	×	×	reset to zero
×	0	1	×	×	set to ABCD
×	0	0	1	×	no change

Q_0 to Q_3 are outputs. A to D are preset inputs.

4510

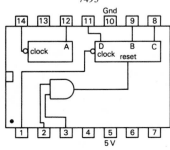

7493

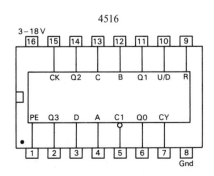

4-bit binary counter

reset inputs		outputs			
pin 2	pin 3	D	C	B	A
1	1	0	0	0	0
0	×	count			
×	0	count			

Output A is to be connected to pin 1.   Pin notation as for 4510.

4516

'×' means 'either state'

Appendix II
Power supplies and the logic box

All the circuits in this book can be constructed with commercially available apparatus. However, the authors assembled their own apparatus and have been using it successfully for a number of years. Details are given below.

Power supplies for logic circuits

Circuits using TTL (systems 1 and 3 in section 1.3) require a regulated 5 V power supply. This can be constructed using the 7805 regulator in the circuit shown.

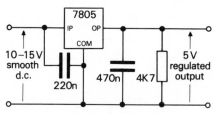

Regulated 5 V power supply for TTL ICs

Construction details for the logic box shown on the front cover

The circuit contains a half-wave rectifier with smoothing followed by the 7805 regulator circuit. Two extra diodes are included to protect the regulator output against inadvertent connection to the wrong terminals of a power supply, which could 'blow' the regulator. The circuit also includes
(a) the four-LED indicator circuit described in section 1.4;
(b) two logic inputs with indicators (the 100 Ω resistors are included in case a socket is 'shorted' to ground);
(c) the debounced push switch described in section 3.3 with an indicator LED.

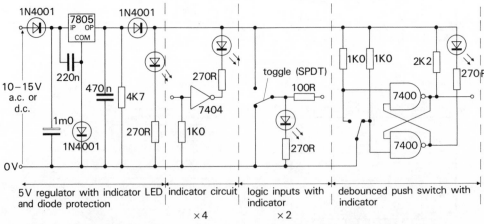

Circuit diagram for the logic box

description	quantity	RS stock number
sloped panel box	1	508–475
protoboard	1	488–618
green LED	3	586–481 (pack of 3)
red LED	4	586–475 (pack of 3)
yellow LED	1	586–497 (pack of 3)
push switch	1	337–942
miniature toggle	2	316–973
red 1 mm socket	7	444–062 (pack of 12)
red 4 mm socket	1	444–646 (pack of 10)
black 4 mm socket	1	444–618 (pack of 10)
1 A, 5 V regulator	1	305–888
7400 quad two-input NAND gate	1	305–490 (pack of 4)
7404 hex inverter	1	305–529 (pack of 4)
100 Ω, 0.5 W resistor	2	132–258 (pack of 10)
270 Ω, 0.5 W resistor	8	132–359 (pack of 10)
1 kΩ, 0.5 W resistor	6	132–494 (pack of 10)
4.7 kΩ, 0.5 W resistor	1	132–652 (pack of 10)
1N4001 diode	3	261–148 (pack of 10)
1000 µF capacitor	1	103–610 (pack of 3)
0.22 µF capacitor	1	113–910 (pack of 5)
0.47 µF capacitor	1	113–926 (pack of 5)
stripboard	1	433–826
6BA bolt (6.4 mm)	1	522–106 (assorted kit of 100)
No. 4 self tap (6.4 mm)	2	522–178 (assorted kit of 100)
6BA nut	1	522–550 (pack of 100)

Parts list for the logic box

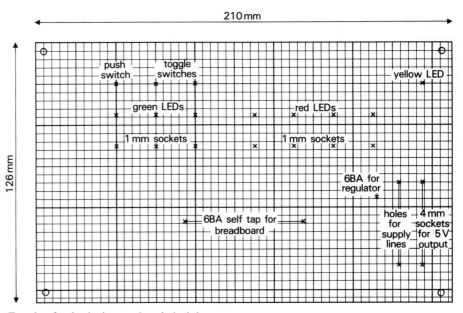

Template for the sloping panel on the logic box

Stripboard for 7-segment display and decoder

The diagram overleaf shows a circuit layout on stripboard for decoding a 4-bit binary number to drive a 7-segment display (RS 587–894). Using a stripboard cutter, cut the copper tracks in 31 places as shown. Solder in the 17 links on the components side, then the 7447 decoder, the 7-segment display and the seven resistors. Finally connect the flying leads to the power supply and the binary inputs (*A* is the least significant bit).

Layout for the stripboard display unit mentioned in section 7.5

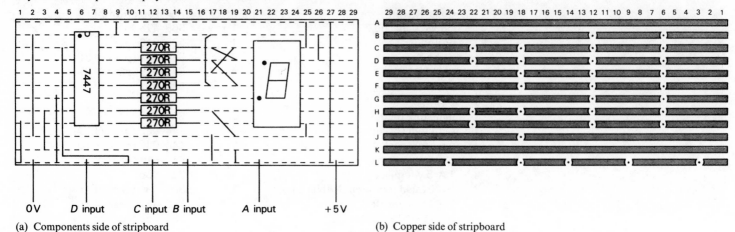

(a) Components side of stripboard

(b) Copper side of stripboard

Power supplies for op-amps

Op-amps require a dual power supply with equal positive and negative voltages relative to ground. A simple circuit that achieves this uses batteries as shown below.

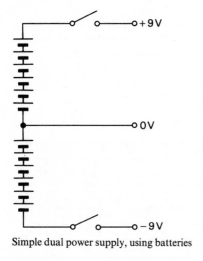

Simple dual power supply, using batteries

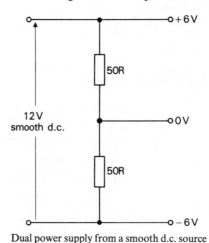

Dual power supply from a smooth d.c. source

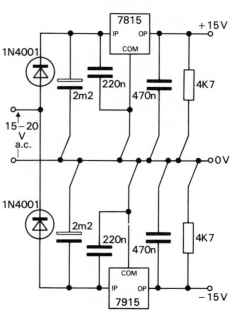

Stabilised supply for advanced work with op-amps

A dual power supply that is suitable for the experiments in this book can be obtained from a single smooth d.c. supply using the middle circuit above.

For more advanced work with op-amps, a stabilised dual supply is required. A suitable circuit for this is also given.

The offset null connections of op-amps

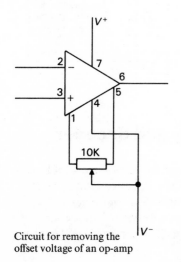

Circuit for removing the offset voltage of an op-amp

When both inputs of an op-amp are at the same potential, the output voltage should be zero. In fact, there is often a small *offset voltage* at the output arising from manufacturing tolerances. For d.c. amplifier circuits this is undesirable, since it gives a finite d.c. output voltage for zero input voltage. To remove or *null* this output voltage, a $10\,\text{k}\Omega$ potentiometer may be connected as shown. However, for the circuits in this book this refinement is not necessary.

Answers to questions

Chapter 1

1 470 Ω

2 See figure 1.

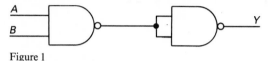

Figure 1

3 '(NOT *A*) AND (NOT *B*)' is a NOR gate. 'NOT (*A* AND *B*)' is a NAND gate. Notice that inverting the inputs has a different result from inverting the output.

4 When the LDR is covered its resistance rises, causing V_{in} to change from high to low. The variable resistor was initially adjusted to make V_{in} above the logic 1 threshold.

5 See figure 2. (Omit the variable resistor for the TTL circuit.) A is the enable position.

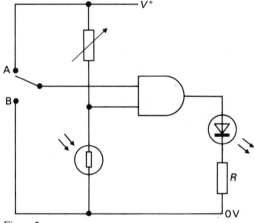

Figure 2

Further questions

1 See figure 3.

Figure 3   (a) AND

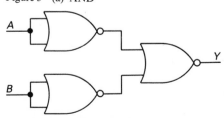

(b) OR

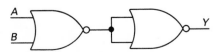

(c) NAND

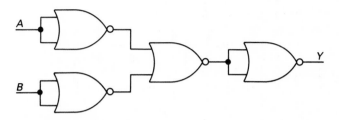

2 Yes. For an AND gate, one input must be held at logic 1 for the other to change the output. For an OR gate, one input must be held at logic 0. With both these gates, the output is the same as the non-fixed input, but with NAND and NOR gates it is inverted.

3

A	*B*	(a) *Y*	(b) *Y*	(c) *Y*	(d) *Y*
0	0	1	1	0	0
0	1	0	1	0	0
1	0	0	1	1	0
1	1	0	0	0	1
		NOR	NAND		AND

See also figure 4.

Figure 4   (a) NOR

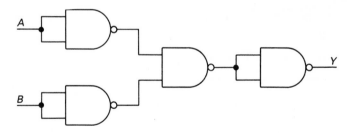

(b) NAND

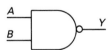

(c)

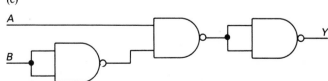

(d) AND

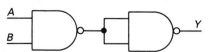

4 See figure 5.

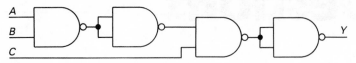

Figure 5

5

| | | | (a) | | | (b) | | | (c) | | |
A	B	C	X	Y	Z	X	Y	Z	X	Y	Z
0	0	0	1	1	1	1	1	0	0	0	1
1	0	0	0	1	0	1	1	0	0	0	1
0	1	0	0	0	0	1	1	0	0	0	1
1	1	0	0	0	0	0	1	0	1	0	1
0	0	1	1	0	0	1	1	0	0	0	1
1	0	1	0	0	0	1	1	0	0	0	1
0	1	1	0	0	0	1	0	0	0	1	1
1	1	1	0	0	0	0	0	1	1	1	0

Figure 1.20(a) is a 3-input NOR gate. Figure 1.20(b) is a 3-input AND gate (if you convert the NOR gate into four NAND gates as in section 1.5, and then cancel out the double negatives, you will arrive at three AND gates). Figure 1.20(c) is a 3-input NAND gate.

6 See figure 6(a) and (b) for two solutions.

Figure 6   (a)

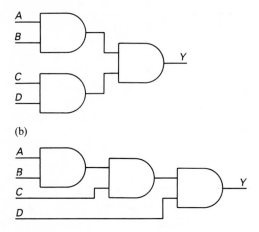

(b)

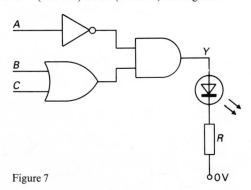

7 $Y = $ (NOT A) AND (B OR C). See figure 7.

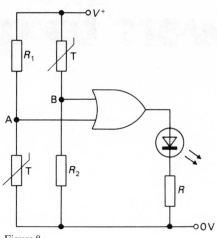

Figure 8

Figure 7

8 (a) Temperature too high. Position A.

(b) The output must be high for the lamp to light. The normal condition has $A = B = 0$ so $R_1 < T$ and $R_2 > T$. See figure 8.

Chapter 2

1

A	B	C	A.B	A.C	A.B+A.C	B+C	A.(B+C)
0	0	0	0	0	0	0	0
0	1	0	0	0	0	1	0
1	0	0	0	0	0	0	0
1	1	0	1	0	1	1	1
0	0	1	0	0	0	1	0
0	1	1	0	0	0	1	0
1	0	1	0	1	1	1	1
1	1	1	1	1	1	1	1

2 $(A+B).(A+C) = A.A+A.C+A.B+B.C$
$$= A(1+C+B)+B.C \qquad \text{since } A.A = A.1$$
$$= A+B.C \qquad \text{since } 1+C+B = 1 \qquad \text{and } A.1 = A$$

3

A	B	$\bar{A}$	$\bar{B}$	$\bar{A}.\bar{B}$	$\overline{\bar{A}.\bar{B}}$	$A+B$	$\bar{A}+\bar{B}$	$\overline{\bar{A}+\bar{B}}$	$A.B$
0	0	1	1	1	0	0	1	0	0
0	1	1	0	0	1	1	1	0	0
1	0	0	1	0	1	1	1	0	0
1	1	0	0	0	1	1	0	1	1

4

A	B	Y
0	0	1
0	1	0
1	0	0
1	1	1

5 $Y = (A$ AND $B)$ OR $((NOT A)$ AND $(NOT B))$
$Y = A.B + \bar{A}.\bar{B}$

6 See figure 9.

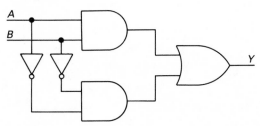

Figure 9

7

A	B	(a) C	D	Y	(b) C	D	Y
0	0	1	0	0	0	1	0
0	1	0	0	1	1	1	1
1	0	0	0	1	1	1	1
1	1	0	1	0	1	0	0

8 The combination of NAND gates is shown in figure 10.

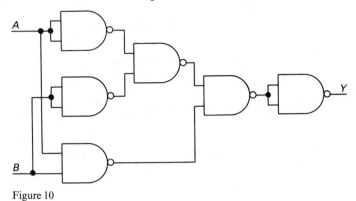

Figure 10

9 $Y = (A+B).\overline{A.B}$

Using de Morgan's theorem,

$Y = (A+B).(\overline{A}+\overline{B})$
$= A.\overline{B}+B.\overline{A}$ since $A.\overline{A} = B.\overline{B} = 0$

10 See figure 11. The broken lines outline combinations of NOR gates that correspond to each of the gates in figure 2.9(a). The diagonal lines show pairs of 'NOT gates' that cancel out, giving the arrangement of gates in figure 2.9(b).

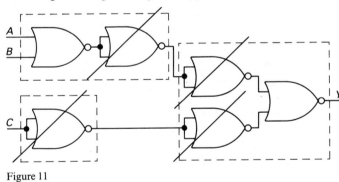

Figure 11

11 There are two solutions to this. One is shown in figure 12.

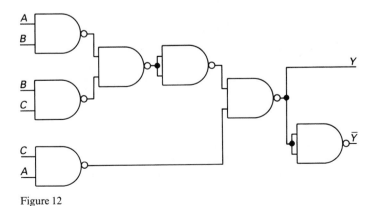

Figure 12

12 DIFFERENCE $= A \oplus B$
   BORROW $= B.D$
See figure 13.

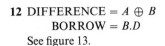

Figure 13

13

binary				denary
(1)	(1)	0	C_{in}	
	1	1	A	3
	0	1	B	1+
				−
1	0	0	S	4
	(1)	(1)	C_{out}	

14 $B = 1001$ $A = 0100$ $\overline{A} = 1011$

binary				denary
0	1	1	(1)	C_{in}	
1	0	0	1	B	9
1	0	1	1	$\overline{A}$	4−
					−
0	1	0	1	S	5
(1)	0	1	1	C_{out}	

15

		A_2	A_1	binary 1	0
		B_2	B_1 $\times$	1	1 $\times$
	C_2	A_2B_1	A_1B_1	1	0
C_3	B_2A_2	B_2A_1	$+$	1 0	$+$
S_4	S_3	S_2	S_1	0 1 1	0

Further questions

1 See figure 14.

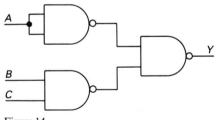

Figure 14

2 The final columns of the two truth tables are shown below.

A	B	C	A OR (B AND C)	(A OR B) AND C
0	0	0	0	0
0	1	0	0	0
1	0	0	1	**0**
1	1	0	1	**0**
0	0	1	0	0
0	1	1	1	1
1	0	1	1	1
1	1	1	1	1

3 Write out the truth table for the EOR gate. Input A is used as a control. You see that input B = output Y when input $A = 0$. With input $A = 1$, the gate acts as an inverter.

4 See figure 15.

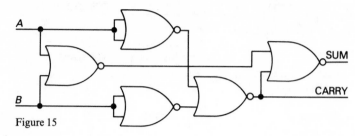

Figure 15

5 See figure 16.

Figure 16

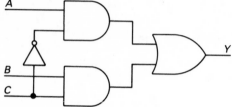

(a) Using AND, NOT and OR gates

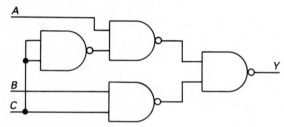

(b) Using NAND gates only

6 (a) $Y = \bar{A} + B.C$
(b) See figure 17.

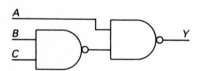

Figure 17

(c) $Y = \overline{A.B.C}$
(d) $\overline{A.B.C} = \bar{A} + \overline{B.C} = \bar{A} + B.C$

7 The half subtractor was shown in figure 13. The full subtractor is shown in figure 18.

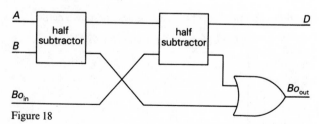

Figure 18

8 Three possibilities are shown in figure 19. Can you show they are all equivalent?

Figure 19   (a)

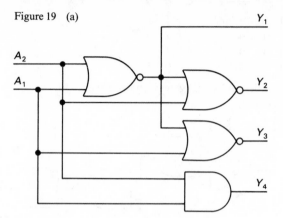

(b)

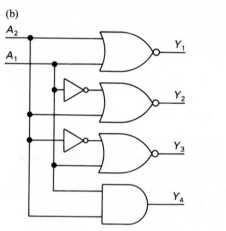

(c)

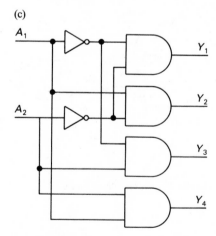

9 See figure 20.

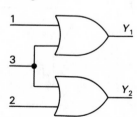

Figure 20

0	1	2	3	Y_1	Y_2
1	0	0	0	0	0
0	1	0	0	1	0
0	0	1	0	0	1
0	0	0	1	1	1

$Y_1 = 1 + 3$ $Y_2 = 2 + 3$

10 See figure 21 for a solution.

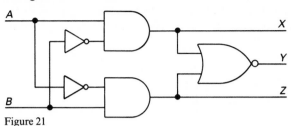

Figure 21

11 (a) See figure 22(a).
(b) See figure 22(b). $Y = 1$ if $A_2 > B_2$ or if $A_2 = B_2$ and $A_1 > B_1$.

Figure 22 (a)

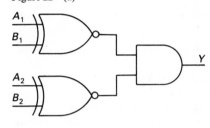

(b)

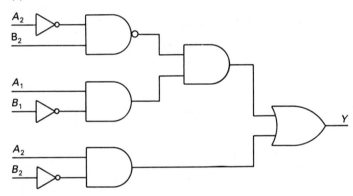

12 See figure 23.
$$Y = A.B.C + A.B.D + B.C.D + A.C.D$$
$$= A.B.(C+D) + C.D.(A+B)$$

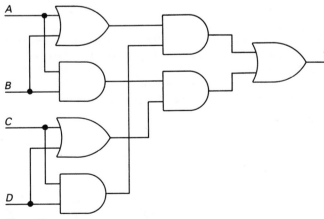

Figure 23

13 For figure 1.20(a) $Z = (\overline{A} + B).(\overline{B} + C) = \overline{(\overline{A} + B) + (\overline{B} + C)}$
$$= \overline{A} + B + C$$

For figure 1.20(b) $Z = \overline{\overline{A.B} + \overline{B.C}} = (A.B).(B.C) = A.B.C$
For figure 1.20(c) $Z = \overline{\overline{(A.B).(B.C)}} = A.B.C$

14 (a) $C = \overline{A.B}$ $\quad D = \overline{\overline{A}.A.B}$ $\quad E = \overline{B.\overline{A.B}}$
$Y = \overline{D.E} = A.\overline{A.B} + B.\overline{A.B}$
$\quad = A.(\overline{A} + \overline{B}) + B.(\overline{A} + \overline{B})$
$\quad = A.\overline{B} + B.\overline{A}$
(b) $\overline{\overline{A.B} + \overline{A.B}} = \overline{\overline{A.B}.\overline{A.B}} = (\overline{A} + B).(A + \overline{B}) = A.B + \overline{A}.\overline{B}$

Chapter 3

1 $Q = \overline{Q} = 1$
2 Nothing: $Q = 1$ and $\overline{Q} = 0$ as before.
3 $Q = \overline{Q} = 1$. This is called the *indeterminate condition*. (See the end of section 3.3.)
4 See figure 24.

pulse number	Q_D	Q_C	Q_B	Q_A
9	1	0	0	1
10	1	0	1	0
11	1	0	1	1
12	1	1	0	0
13	1	1	0	1
14	1	1	1	0
15	1	1	1	1

Figure 24

5 The circuit acts as a down-counter.
6 See figure 25. The clock is inverted to make the counter trigger on the rising edge of the clock pulse.

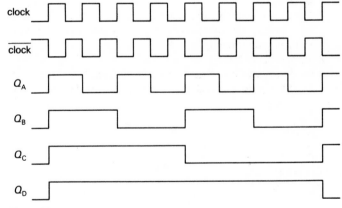

Figure 25

7 Output Q_C changes logic state after every four clock pulses, Q_D after every eight clock pulses.
8 Use $\overline{Q}_B$ and $\overline{Q}_D$ as inputs to the resetting gate, instead of Q_B and Q_D.
9 Connect Q_A, Q_B and Q_C to a triple (N)AND gate but clear only Q_B and Q_C, not Q_A.
10 Yes, it would still count. (See figure 3.22.)
11 Initially $\overline{Q} = A = 1$, $Q = 0$, C is uncharged and $B = 0$. When A becomes 0, Q goes to 1, B goes to 1 and $\overline{Q}$ goes to 0. C charges, so V_B falls towards 0 until the gate switches $\overline{Q}$ to 1. Q remains at 1 whatever A is, until $\overline{Q}$ returns to 1. $\overline{Q}$ still returns to 1 even if $A = 0$.

Further questions

1 See figure 26.

Figure 26   (a)

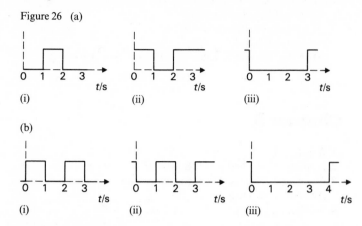

(i)   (ii)   (iii)

(b)

(i)   (ii)   (iii)

2 Check that the pulse sequence of figure 3.10 is applicable.

3 The circuit is a *D* flip-flop made of NAND gates. *A* is the *D* input and *B* the clock input.

4 Connect $\bar{Q}$ to the clock input instead of Q for each flip-flop and invert the clock pulse. To reset to 9, connect outputs Q_A to Q_D to a four-input NAND gate. Connect the output of the NAND gate to the first and last flip-flop presets. NB In practice the counter may reset between 8 and 7 if all the outputs rise to logic 1 for an instant at switching.

5 (a) Three, four and five flip-flops.
   (b) $N = 2^n - 1$, where N is the maximum count and n is the number of flip-flops.

6 In a 2-bit counter, output Q_A is an octave higher than output Q_B so the first two sections of the circuit in figure 3.17 would be suitable.

7 The decade counter circuits shown in figures 3.20 and 3.21 can be used, except that the input to the resetting gate must be moved from output Q_B to Q_A.

8 (a) See figure 27(a).
   (b) See figure 27(b). The astable is made from NAND gates. If NOR gates are used, Q_D should be connected to the enable, not $\bar{Q}_D$.

Figure 27   (a)

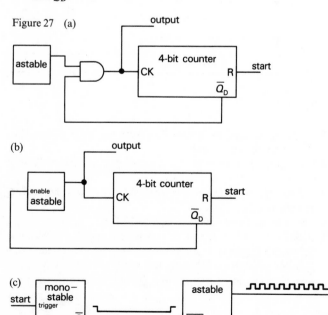

(b)

(c)

(c) See figure 27(c). Use NOR gates for the astable. In the counter circuit, the pulse length is determined by the astable. The monostable and astable must be adjusted carefully to fit an 8:1 ratio.

9 See figure 28.

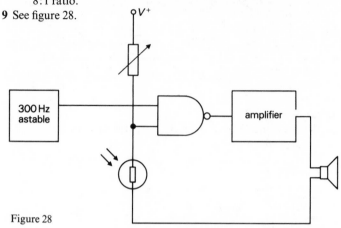

Figure 28

10 (a) When the read-write line is at logic 0, it will act as a *read* only; at logic 1, it will act as a *write* or a *read*.
   (b) To write, data is accepted when the address and read–write lines are at logic 1. To read, only the address needs to be at logic 1. The cell retains its information after a read-only command. See figure 29 for a circuit in which the read facility is disabled when writing.

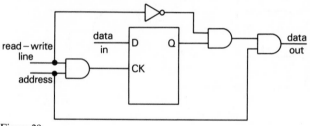

Figure 29

Chapter 4

1 More negative.

2 (a) 0 V   (b) 10 V   (c) 0 V

3 $0.1V^-$ to $0.1V^+$.

4 200 kΩ

5 5000. However, with $R_f = 50$ MΩ, R_f would be much greater than the input resistance so the simple theory would not apply.

6 See figure 30.

7 The input resistor R_1 has a value of 10 kΩ and the input resistance of the op-amp can be assumed to be infinite (rule 1).

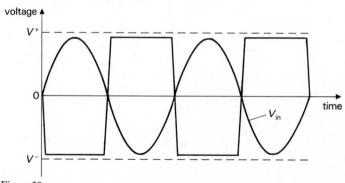

Figure 30

8 $0.1V^-$ to $0.1V^+$.

9 The gain is unity and the input resistance is infinite for an ideal op-amp.

10 $V_{\text{out}} = -10V_{\text{in}}$

11 $V_{\text{out}} = -10(V_1 + V_2)$

12 $V_{\text{out}} = -(V_1 + 10V_2)$

13 The circuit will switch from V^- to V^+ as V_{in} approaches V^+, and from V^+ to V^- when V_{in} approaches V^-.

14 The input voltage does not vary enough to trigger the circuit. V_{out} remains constant.

15 Use rules 1 and 2 and refer to the explanation of the non-inverting Schmitt trigger.

16 Reduce the value of either resistance R or capacitance C to one-fifth of its former value.

17 Changing the ratio of the two resistors will change the place on the charging curve at which the capacitor is switched from charging to discharging.

18 The circuit in figure 4.21 can be used with the 1 MΩ resistor replaced by a variable resistor.

19 No.

Further questions

1 (a) Figure 4.8, with $R_f = 300\,\text{k}\Omega$, is a suitable circuit.
(b) Figure 4.10, with $R_f = 290\,\text{k}\Omega$, is a suitable circuit.

2 In the dark, $R_2 > R_1$, which drives V_{out} to V^+; when it is illuminated, $R_2 < R_1$, which drives V_{out} to V^-. The device is a light-operated switch that could switch on a lamp connected between V_{out} and V^- when it becomes dark.

3 Figure 4.18, with $R_{\text{in}}/R_f = 0.2$, is a suitable circuit.

4 Figure 4.15 with $R_1 = 10\,\text{k}\Omega$, $R_2 = 5\,\text{k}\Omega$ and $R_f = 50\,\text{k}\Omega$, is a suitable circuit.

5 The closed-loop gain should be $1.0\,\text{V}/20\,\text{mV} = 50$.

6 See figure 31. The mark-to-space ratio should be 5.

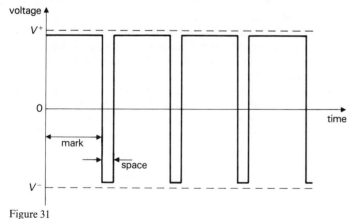

Figure 31

Chapter 5

1 See figure 32. The maximum current flow, I, through the 1 kΩ

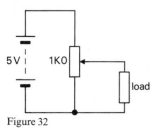

Figure 32

potentiometer is 50 mA. The minimum power rating is
$$P = I^2R = (5 \times 10^{-2})^2 \times 10^3 = 2.5\,\text{W}$$

2 The voltage across the diode is 0.6 V (one 'diode drop'). The voltage across the resistor is
$$5.0\,\text{V} - 0.6\,\text{V} = 4.4\,\text{V}.$$
The power dissipated by the resistor is
$$\frac{(\text{Voltage across resistor})^2}{R} = \frac{4.4^2}{100} = 0.2\,\text{W}$$

So the minimum power rating of the resistor is 0.2 W.

3 The forward resistance of the diode is obtained from the characteristic.
$$\text{At } 10\,\text{mA} \qquad R_f = \frac{V_f}{I_f} = \frac{0.7}{10^{-2}} = 70\,\Omega$$
$$\text{and at } 40\,\text{mA} \qquad R_f = 18\,\Omega$$

4 (a) $V_X = 0.7 \times 1 = 0.7\,\text{V}$
$V_Y = 2.0 \times 10 \times 10^{-3} = 2 \times 10^{-2}\,\text{V} = 20\,\text{mV}$

(b) $\dfrac{V_Y}{V_X} = \dfrac{2 \times 10^{-2}}{0.7} = 3$ per cent

(c) Current through the diode is
$$I = \frac{V_Y}{R} = \frac{2 \times 10^{-2}}{1} = 2 \times 10^{-2}\,\text{A} = 20\,\text{mA}$$

5 The most noticeable effect of swapping the Y-input and common connections would be to invert the characteristic displayed on the screen. An advantage would be that V_X would be the voltage across the diode alone.

6 The power dissipated by a Zener diode is $P = VI$. So the maximum current is
$$I = \frac{P_{\text{max}}}{V} = \frac{5 \times 10^{-1}}{5.1} = 0.1\,\text{A}$$

7 The time constant for capacitor discharge is
$$CR = 5 \times 10^{-4} \times 10^2 = 5 \times 10^{-2} = 50\,\text{ms}$$
which is 2.5 times the period of the supply.

8 If the bulb is disconnected, $V_{\text{out}} = 6.5\,\text{V}$ steady d.c.

9 (a) The time constant is reduced by a factor of 10, to 5 ms.
(b) See figure 33.

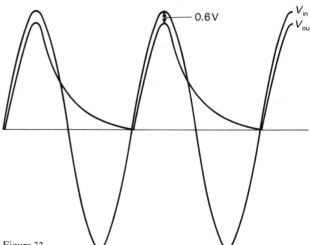

Figure 33

(c) The bulb becomes dimmer because the average value of V_{out} is less.

10 When the transistor is switched off, the power dissipated is
$$V_{\text{ce}}I_{\text{c}} = 5 \times 0 = 0\,\text{W}$$

When the transistor is switched on, the power dissipated is
$V_{ce}I_c = 0.2 \times 1 = 0.2\,\text{W}$.

11 The power dissipated is
$V_{ce}I_c = 5 \times 160 \times 10^{-3} = 0.8\,\text{W}$
The power is the maximum for the 2N3053. The current is much less than the maximum rating.

12 Maximum current through potentiometer is

$$I = \sqrt{\frac{P_{max}}{R}} = \sqrt{\frac{0.25}{10^3}} = 16\,\text{mA}$$

Minimum resistance of load is

$$R_1 = \frac{V}{I} = \frac{5}{16 \times 10^{-3}} = 310\,\Omega$$

13 (a) With no load, the current through diode is the same as the current through resistor, which is

$$\frac{\text{p.d. across resistor}}{R} = \frac{5}{100} = 50\,\text{mA}$$

(b) Voltage across load $= 5.1\,\text{V}$

Current through load $= \dfrac{V}{R} = \dfrac{5.1}{10^3} = 5.1\,\text{mA}$

Current through diode $=$ no-load current $- 5.1\,\text{mA} = 45\,\text{mA}$.

(c) The maximum load current before diode ceases to conduct is 50 mA. The minimum resistance is

$$R_1 = \frac{V_1}{I_{max}} = \frac{5.1}{50 \times 10^{-3}} = 100\,\Omega$$

14 (a) From 0 to 5 V the lamp gets brighter and the Zener diode does not conduct. From 5 to 12 V the lamp remains the same and the Zener diode conducts progressively more current.

(b) When 12 V is applied, the lamp is slightly under-run at 5 V. The voltage across the resistor is 7 V, giving a power

$$\frac{V^2}{R} = \frac{7^2}{100} = 0.5\,\text{W}$$

and a current

$$I = \frac{V}{R} = \frac{7}{100} = 0.07\,\text{A}$$

These are well within the limits of the Zener diode.

(c) The voltage across the lamp never exceeds 0.6 V. Above 0.6 V, the Zener diode conducts and most of the voltage is dropped across the resistor.

(d) At 12 V the voltage across the resistor is 11.4 V, giving a power

$$\frac{V^2}{R} = \frac{11.4^2}{100} = 1.3\,\text{W}$$

This exceeds the power rating of the resistor.

15 (a) When $V_{in} = 0\,\text{V}$, $V_{out} = -0.6\,\text{V}$ and $V_{ce} = 5.6\,\text{V}$. The p.d. across the loudspeaker is $5 - 0.6 = 4.4\,\text{V}$, so the current through the loudspeaker is

$$I = \frac{V}{R} = \frac{4.4}{75} = 59\,\text{mA}$$

Power dissipated by transistor is
$V_{ce}I_c = 5.6 \times 59 \times 10^{-3} = 0.33\,\text{W}$
Power dissipated by loudspeaker is
$4.4 \times 59 \times 10^{-3} = 0.26\,\text{W}$

(b) When a signal is applied, the average powers dissipated are the same as in part (a).

Further questions

1 When point A is more than 1.2 V positive with respect to point B, diodes D_2 and D_4 conduct. When B is more than 1.2 V positive with respect to A, diodes D_1 and D_3 conduct. The input and output voltage waveforms are shown in figure 34.

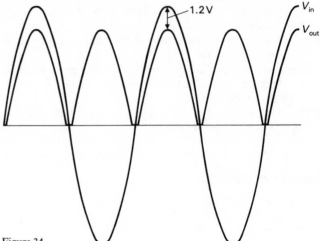

Figure 34

2 The voltage across the meter for a full-scale deflection is

$$V = IR = 10^{-4} \times 10^3 = 0.1\,\text{V}.$$

Under these conditions, the diodes do not conduct. One of the diodes begins to conduct when $V = 0.6\,\text{V}$; that is, when the current through the meter is six times that required for maximum deflection. After that, the voltage remains at about 0.6 V and any current in excess of 600 μA flows through the conducting diode.

3 If either of the diodes is connected to 0 V it will conduct and the voltage of Q will be 0.6 V (logic 0). If both diodes are connected to $+5\,\text{V}$, neither will conduct, no current flows and Q will be at 5 V (logic 1). It is therefore an AND gate, and the truth table is the same as in figure 1.10.

4 Assume that both the capacitors are discharged and the supply is going through zero in the negative direction (see figure 35). As the supply voltage, V_{in}, becomes maximum negative (A) positive charge flows through D_1 onto the right-hand plate of C_1. During the next half cycle (B) the left-hand side of C_1 rises through a voltage of twice the amplitude of the supply. Positive charge flows off the right-hand plate of C_1, through D_2 and onto the upper

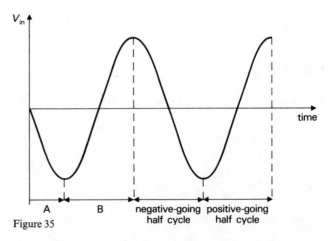

Figure 35

plate of C_2. Subsequently, C_1 charges via D_1 during part of negative-going half cycles and partly discharges through D_2 into C_2 during part of positive-going half cycles. After a number of cycles, C_2 is charged up to twice the amplitude of the supply (less 1.2 V, the voltage drop across the two diodes).

5 (a) At A, $V_{in} = 0.6$ V

(b) At B, $I_C = \dfrac{V}{R_2} = \dfrac{5}{10^3} = 5$ mA

(c) $I_b = \dfrac{I_c}{h_{FE}} = \dfrac{5 \times 10^{-3}}{100} = 50\,\mu$A

(d) $V_{in} = 0.6 + I_b R_1 = 0.6 + 50 \times 10^{-6} \times 10^4 = 1.1$ V

(e) Voltage gain is

$$\frac{\Delta V_{out}}{\Delta V_{in}} = \frac{5}{0.5} = 10$$

6 (a) Current gain $= h_{FE} \times h_{FE} = 150 \times 150 = 2.3 \times 10^4$

(b) The current amplified by the first transistor is fed into the second transistor, which amplifies it further.

(c) For the transistor to conduct, V_{in} must be greater than two 'diode drops', i.e. $V_{in} > 2 \times 0.6$ V $= 1.2$ V

7 See figure 36. When the LDR has resistance 4000 Ω,

$$I_b = \frac{V}{R} = \frac{4.4}{4000} = 1.1\,\text{mA}$$

$$I_c = h_{FE} \times I_b = 100 \times 1.1 = 110\,\text{mA}$$

This is sufficient to operate the relay and saturate the transistor. The diode across the relay coil is essential to prevent large induced e.m.f.s when the coil is switched off. (For a more complete explanation of this see an A level textbook, under 'inductors'.)

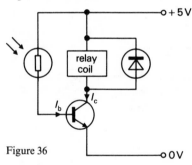

Figure 36

8 (a) For the transistor to conduct, either A or B must be 1.2 V positive (i.e. two 'diode drops'). The truth table is shown in figure 1.10. It is a NOR gate.

(b) For the transistor to conduct, C must be 1.2 V positive. If either A or B is connected to 0 V, C is at 0.6 V, the transistor is cut-off. The truth table is shown in figure 1.10. It is a NAND gate.

9 Hint: the two transistors are acting as two inverters, producing positive feedback.

10 Hint: the waveforms at X and Y are shown in figure 37.

Chapter 6

1 At 1600 Hz $\quad Z = \dfrac{1}{2\pi f C} = \dfrac{1}{2\pi \times 1600 \times 10^{-8}} = 10\,\text{k}\Omega$

At 200 Hz $\quad Z = 80\,\text{k}\Omega$
At 6400 Hz $\quad Z = 2.5\,\text{k}\Omega$
The capacitor would have an impedance of 1 kΩ at 1.6 kHz.

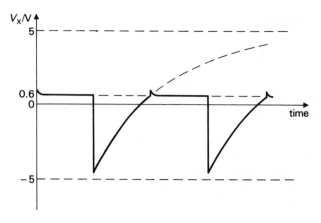

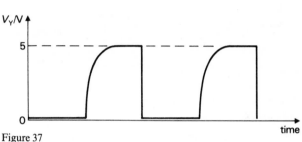

Figure 37

2 See figure 38. The output would be about one-eighth of the input when $f = 8 \times 1.6 = 12.8$ kHz.

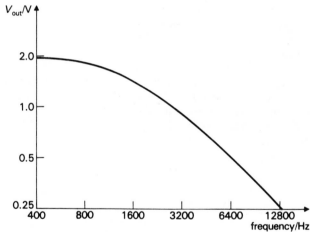

Figure 38

3 $Z = 2\pi f L$, so if the frequency is halved, the impedance is halved. So $Z = 80\,\Omega$ at 500 Hz.
If $f = 0$, $Z = 0$.

4 (a) The diode loads the tuned circuit (i.e. takes current), making it less selective and lowering the alternating voltage across it.

(b) A component of the signal from the diode to the 741 is d.c.

(c) The power amplification is inefficient because a class A amplifier is being used.

5 (a) The FET source follower circuit does not load the tuned circuit, so the signal is larger and better selected.

(b) $R_2 C_2$ removes the d.c. component (1 or 2 V) of the signal from the source follower.

(c) $R_4 C_4$ removes the d.c. component from the demodulated signal.

(d) The push-pull circuit can deliver more power to the loudspeaker than the class A amplifier without getting too hot.

Chapter 7

1 Use ten *D* flip-flops, with Q_{10} connected to the input. Preset Q_1 to 1.

2 Use ten *D* flip-flops as a twisted-ring counter. Output at Q_{10}.

3 It is analogous to a twisted strip of paper, with its ends stuck together. One side of the paper corresponds to logic 0, the other to logic 1.

4 See figure 39. The arrangement shown uses TTL 7476 *JK* falling-edge triggered flip-flops.

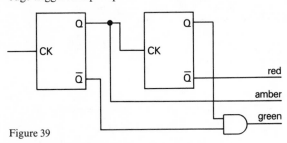

Figure 39

5 The whole *cycle* of the counter is used.

6 See figure 40.

Figure 40

7 The timer switches when all four inputs are 1. Denary 12 is binary 1100. As inputs *A* and *B* are always 1, all four inputs become 1 between 11 and 12 seconds after reset.

8 A four-input NAND gate.

9 None, because the *spike* is negative.

10 See figure 41.

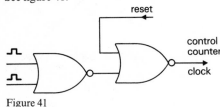

Figure 41

11 The counter will give the same result with rising or falling edges only when the pulses are of equal length.

Further questions

1 Binary 0000 is given by the output of the AND gate with inputs $\bar{Q}_A$, $\bar{Q}_B$, $\bar{Q}_C$, $\bar{Q}_D$; binary 0110 is given by the output of the AND gate with inputs $\bar{Q}_A$, Q_B, Q_C, $\bar{Q}_D$; etc.

2 See figure 42.

3 See figure 43. To vary the response time interval, alter the value of the *RC* combination that governs the length of the monostable output pulse.

4 (a) Another twisted-ring counter. Try it.
   (b) V_{out} is a staircase waveform that rises with each clock pulse (an analogue output for a digital input).

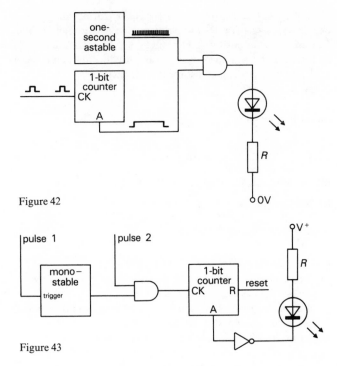

Figure 42

Figure 43

(c) A synchronous binary counter. Work it through. (Remember that *Q* only changes when $J = K = 1$.)
(d) The circuit produces three pulses and then stops.

5 See figure 44 for a possible solution.

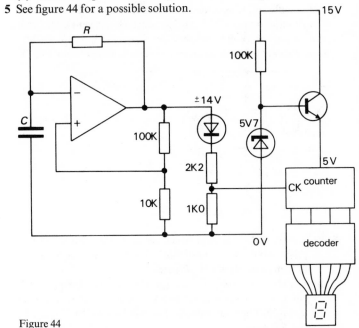

Figure 44

Chapter 8

1 With the potentiometer wiper at end X, the closed-loop gain is 51; at end Y, the closed-loop gain is unity.

2 The capacitor enables an alternating voltage to be fed to the input without changing the d.c. voltage defined by the two 100 kΩ resistors.

3 The gain is 220 kΩ/10 kΩ = 22.

4 With zero input, the emitters of the two transistors are at a potential of $V^+/2$. With no capacitor, therefore, the loudspeaker would carry a steady current of $V^+/2R$, where *R* is its resistance.

With the capacitor in series with the loudspeaker, only alternating currents flow in the loudspeaker.

5 $T = 1.1\, RC$. If, for example, $R = 1\,M\Omega$,

$$C = \frac{0.5}{1.1 \times 10^6} = 0.45\,\mu F$$

(The nearest value available commercially would be $0.47\,\mu F$.)

6 The maximum frequency $= \dfrac{1.44}{3 \times 10^4 \times 10^{-7}} = 480\,Hz$

The minimum frequency of operation is 14 Hz.

7 $T = 1.1\, RC = 0.52\,ms$

8 The capacitor must be large enough to damp out unsteady readings of the voltmeter at low pulse rates, but small enough not to give too long a response time.

9 Provide a diode in parallel with the variable resistor R in order to discharge capacitor C quickly whilst retaining a slow charging rate.

10 $f = 1/(2\pi RC)$, therefore RC must be 1.6×10^{-4} s. One pair of suitable values is $R = 10\,k\Omega$, $C = 16\,nF$.

11 See figure 45.

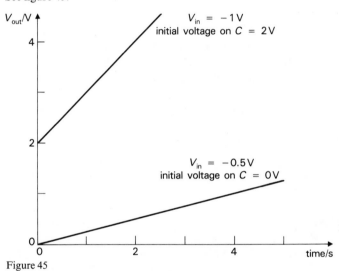

Figure 45

12 See figure 45. The initial voltage is the analogue of the object having an initial speed.

13 When $RC = 0.1$ s, $V_{out} = 10\displaystyle\int V_{in}\,dt$.

14 The system is the analogue of exponential decay. Examples of corresponding physical situations are radioactive decay, the voltage across a capacitor discharging through a resistor and the level of water in a cylindrical bucket with a hole in its base.

15 The output voltage V_{out} is the analogue of I in figure 8.16. The input voltage p is the analogue of E/L in figure 8.16. The feedback voltage q is the analogue of R/L in figure 8.16.

16 Disconnect the potentiometer R_q from the output of op-amp 1 and connect it to V^-.

Further questions

1 The period of the 555 astable is 0.72 s, and the period of the 555 monostable is 0.52 s. Figure 46 shows the waveforms at A and B.

2 One or other diode will conduct when there is more than 0.6 V across the pair of diodes. Thus the gain is 47 when V_{out} is less than 0.6 V and 2.2 when V_{out} is greater than 0.6 V. (See figure 47.)

3 See figure 48.

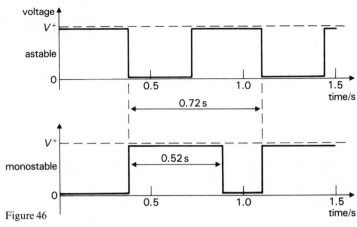

Figure 46

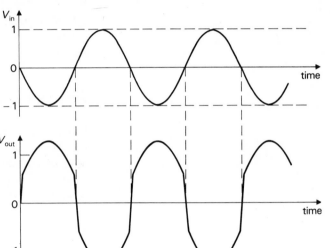

Figure 47

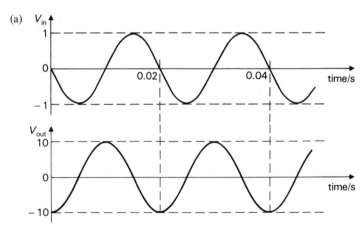

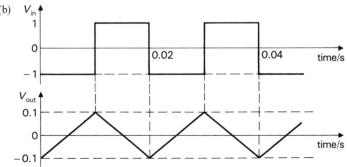

Figure 48

Further reading

For the student

Duncan, T., *Success in Electronics*, John Murray, 1983
Plant, M., *Op-amp Applications*, National Centre for School Technology, 1978
Ritz, H., *Digibook*, Elektor Publications Ltd., Canterbury 1978
Schools Council, *Modular Courses in Technology: Instrumentation*, Oliver & Boyd, 1983
Sinclair, I. R., *Practical Electronics Handbook*, Newnes Technical, 1980

For project work

Duncan, T., *Adventures with Digital Electronics*, John Murray, 1982
Duncan, T., *Adventures with Microelectronics*, John Murray, 1981
Microelectronics Education Programme, *Microelectronics – Practical Approaches for Schools and Colleges*, BP Educational Service, 1981
Schools Council, *Project Technology: Photocell Applications*, Hodder and Stoughton, 1973
300 Circuits for the Home Constructor, Elektor Publications Ltd., Canterbury 1979
301 Circuits: Practical Electronic Circuits for the Home Constructor, Elektor Publications Ltd., Canterbury, 1983

For the teacher

Brimicombe, M. W., *Electronic Systems*, Nelson, 1985
Dance, J. B., *Op-amps: Their Principles and Applications*, Newnes Technical, 1978
Horowitz, P., and Hill, W., *The Art of Electronics*, Cambridge University Press, 1980
Jones, M. H., *A Practical Introduction to Electronic Circuits*, Cambridge University Press, 1981
Millman, J., *Microelectronics: Digital and Analog Circuits and Systems*, McGraw-Hill, 1979
Sparkes, R. A., *Microelectronics: A Practical Introduction*, Hutchinson, 1984

For reference

Lancaster, D., *CMOS Cookbook*, Howard W. Sams, Indianapolis, USA, 1977
Lancaster, D., *TTL Cookbook*, Howard W. Sams, Indianapolis, USA, 1974
Data Sheet Book, Elektor Publications Ltd., Canterbury, 1983

Index